Watching the Leaves Dance

Leaves Dance

GRAHAM STOKES

HAWKER PUBLICATIONS
LONDON

First published in 2017 by
Hawker Publications Ltd
Culvert House
Culvert Road
London SW11 5DH
Tel: 020 7720 2108
www.careinfo.org

British Library Cataloguing in Publication Data
A catalogue record for this book is available from the
British Library

ISBN 9781874790402

Cover design by www.wheelhousedesign.co.uk
Editing and typesetting by Prepare to Publish Ltd,
mail@preparetopublish.com

Set in Stempel Garamond

Printed and bound in Great Britain by Short Run Press, Exeter

Watching the Leaves Dance's companion volume
And Still the Music Plays (ISBN 9781874790884) can be purchased
from Hawker Publications by visiting the website www.careinfo.org
or telephoning 020 7720 2108 from within the UK or (44) 20 7720
2108 from all other countries.

Contents

Foreword

BY KEITH OLIVER

As a primary school teacher and headteacher for over 35 years I am aware of the potential of storytelling, especially if the stories are true or have a meaning behind them, which is one reason why I am delighted and honoured to write this foreword to what is a really enlightening publication. Alongside this, as a person who has lived with a diagnosis of dementia for six years I recognise the need for champions like Professor Graham Stokes to help articulate and place our thoughts, experiences, hopes and fears where they are most likely to be considered and will support others. Professionals, through talking to people living the experience of dementia, know something of what it is like, but cannot fully comprehend the impact of the condition. It is only people such as those whose stories are told in this book, and those who share our lives and care, who really know and understand, which again adds to the importance of this book.

Soon after my diagnosis I bought and read Graham's book *And Still the Music Plays* and I found it both uplifting and illuminating, in that it opened my eyes, mind and heart to those whose lives we entered into. To allow the characters described in his latest book to express themselves as clearly as they do, Graham again displays the range of skills I have witnessed first hand in meetings and committees where we share a desire to make a difference for the many people living with dementia in the UK. Both Graham and I often refer to the work of Tom Kitwood and person-centred care. I carry in my diary the Kitwood flower with love at its centre, surrounded by petals highlighting comfort, identity, occupation, inclusion and attachment. Professor Stokes's latest book totally endorses all of these.

Watching the Leaves Dance takes us once again, not into the realm of patients, carers or service users but into the lives of people, and whether you are a person affected by dementia, someone working in the world of dementia or an interested 'outsider' (at the moment!) there is something for everyone to take and benefit from reading *Watching the Leaves Dance*.

Keith Oliver is an Alzheimer's Society Ambassador and Kent and Medway Partnership Trust NHS Dementia Service User Envoy

Introduction

We understand dementia as a human, subjective experience as distinct from a neuropathological process having listened to and learnt from the experiences and tales of people affected by dementia, both those who care and those who need that support and care. *Watching the Leaves Dance* is an anthology of some of these stories, accounts that put the person first – I will always owe Mrs S* an immeasurable debt of gratitude – and places dementia in its true perspective. Namely, accepting it is a progressive intellectual disability that most people facing it experience, endure and even find themselves tested by, while some are inspired and motivated not only to help themselves but also those who are equally affected but are less resilient through their own doubts and flaws.

Yet why write stories? First, as Oliver Sacks observed in his book *The Man Who Mistook His Wife for a Hat*, stories make it possible for us to "have a 'who' as well as a 'what'", and each story in this book and its companion volume *And Still the Music Plays* is a testimony to the experiences of those who have become "travellers to unimaginable lands".

The second reason is that by telling richly personal stories we continue to undermine the myth that dementia is about pathology, medicines and a 'one size fits all' approach to how we enable, support and care for people with dementia. Describing something about those involved restores them to the centre of our understanding.

Person-centred approaches have been around for nearly 30 years yet it seems we still have some way to go, for barely a day goes by when there are not compelling examples of the needs and feelings of people with dementia, especially as they progress to advanced stages, being disregarded, marginalised or not even being acknowledged. There is a need still to give dementia a human face. Stories that reveal how lives are affected by dementia in ways that can be unexpected, sometimes cruel, on occasions uplifting but always life changing. Stories of ordinary people now living extraordinary lives.

And what these stories tell us is that people with dementia can be a puzzle, but why should it be otherwise? We are all complicated. Our partners, family and friends may at times be mystified by what we do or say. We at times may surprise ourselves, asking 'why did I do that?', and sometimes being equally mystified by the answer. So why should a person with dementia be anything other than similarly complicated in what they say and do?

By getting close to people with dementia, seeing and listening rather than looking and hearing but learning nothing, the more you appreciate that each person embarks on their *own* journey with dementia. All are resourced differently to cope and as such some cope less well than others, while on occasions we are given the opportunity to wonder at the extraordinary fortitude of the human spirit. In all instances and at all times knowing who people with dementia are must be the guiding principle that governs whatever we do to help them negotiate what will one day be a harrowing entry into a world of not knowing.

And to truly appreciate this we must not be seduced by what is obvious. Yes, a person with dementia's intellectual powers are failing, that is clear, but we must never become preoccupied with a person's dementia to the exclusion of all else. If we do, all we see is difference, and if all we see is difference then we know we share nothing in common and the danger is that we start to act and react to people with dementia in ways that are insensitive and unthinking to the point where we may disregard them as people like ourselves.

Instead we understand the person as someone who is trying to communicate who they are and who they have always been while losing the capacity to remember all that once anchored them in place and time, as their language crumbles and conversation is challenged, and as their ability to think and reason slips away and risk and vulnerability surface. Their behaviour and feelings may present as strange and disproportionate but this is not testimony to the person having been lost.

Watching the Leaves Dance begins by looking at how four people – Isabel, Jimmy, Lucy and Caroline – slowly became aware that something was not right and having been given a diagnosis attempted to cope in their own ways with a destiny that none had ever contemplated. Sometimes alone, at other times supported by families affected by the heavy emotional demands dementia can place on partners, siblings and children. And we find that the commitment to care that surfaces flows in both directions for as Isabel reminded me, "I've not only got myself to think about."

The next two stories embrace 'A question of diagnosis' as inexplicable and troubling behaviours cause worry and distress for family and professional caregivers alike. The theme of 'Dementia together' explores how 'I have dementia' evolves into 'we have dementia' as partners struggle to come to terms with what is happening now, and in one instance a husband questions the very fabric of his marriage of nearly 60 years, while a family is torn apart by dementia.

Voltaire said judge a man by his questions rather than by his answers. 'The search for meaning' reveals how the most bizarre and out-of-character behaviours resonate with meaning, a meaning that is founded on who the person is and how they want their life to be, even if for many families it feels very different, with the person's strange and unfathomable behaviour being taken as testimony that their loved one has departed. As one distraught wife said, "This bloody dementia has taken my Alan."

Finally, 'Touching lives' looks into the world of professional care. Care that is too often undervalued and denigrated when it is a role that most could never do.

Many fail to appreciate that we have placed society's most vulnerable adults into the hands of these professionals. In these stories we meet some truly excellent practitioners, some who believed that much more could be done to give people with dementia a life worth living, sometimes in the most trying and challenging of circumstances. Yet there will always be lessons to be learned and places where angels fear to tread.

For some who read this book the experience will have been an epiphany. If it has been, might we all now hold the conviction that what we do to help people with dementia is diminished only by the limits we place on our ambition, imagination and humanity.

Graham Stokes, September 2016

* Stokes G (1995) Incontinence or not? Person first, dementia second. *Journal of Dementia Care* 3(2) 20-21.

PART I

Journeys start

*"You have to begin to lose your memory,
if only in bits and pieces, to realise that
memory makes our lives"*
– LUIS BUNUEL

ONE

Life is not fair

I sabel felt her life was falling apart. A willowy woman with wild unkempt hair and piercing blue eyes, she was desperate to know what was happening to her. While I didn't share her desperation, despite times when I would come close, I was curious. Referred by her GP because of a head injury sustained in a car accident, this 43-year-old woman was a conundrum, not simply because her test results did not match the brain trauma her GP reported, but because the problems she was reporting and the struggles she was having simply shouldn't have been happening.

Four years earlier she had been the front seat passenger in a car coming home from a party. For the first time in ages she felt good about herself. A mother of two sons, she had been divorced for a year. The separation had been bitter. The boys had become a battlefield full of acrimony and blame, and while that was all in the past and Luke and James were now settled with Isabel, she still felt rubbish. She'd never had a lot of confidence and her low self-esteem made her vulnerable. It probably started with the divorce of her own parents when she was 15: the ideas which resonated most with her were 'not good enough', 'could do better', 'they don't really want you'.

It was a Sunday when her mother packed her cases and walked out, to live with another man. There had been no argument that Isabel had been aware of. She just appeared at the bottom of the stairs and announced she was going. Isabel pleaded with her not to but, no, she was leaving. Hurt and angry, she refused to even consider her mum's request that she came with her. Days later her father announced in a manner that was quite matter of fact that he had been offered a short-term contract and had to leave for Aberdeen. He'd be away for a couple of months. All Isabel heard was 'Aberdeen! Months!'. Her father said he had no choice. And deep down she knew this was true for this was his life and this was the way family life had always been. Weeks together, months apart. It's what happens when your father works in the oil industry and he has to go wherever the work takes him. She had never found the separation easy. It was difficult because she had no brothers or sisters and her mother would fall so quiet when dad was away.

Feeling alone, as a young girl she would look at the moon, thinking that's what her dad was also doing and somehow it brought him closer to her. As years passed and she got accustomed to the absences it had become easier, if never easy. But please, not now. It could have been worse, for it could have been Saudi, Nigeria or some other faraway place, but Aberdeen was still many miles away. He told Isabel she would have to stay with her mother and 'Tony'. She protested that she would be fine living by herself for a couple of months but her father would have none of it. So, on another upsetting Sunday with tears flowing and feeling unbridled bitterness toward her mother, she packed her things and walked out of her bedroom blissfully ignorant that she was leaving her room for the final time.

With hindsight, and a maturity she did not then possess, she knows she never gave Tony and her mother a chance, but back then she was an angry, confused and increasingly insecure teenager who blamed her mother and 'him' for turning her life upside down. Could her mother not see the extent of her betrayal? Shutting herself away in her 'new room' that she was determined would never truly become hers, the days and weeks passed slowly. As did the months, many months! Her dad, who had never been the most communicative of men, would telephone occasionally, yet rarely did he mention when he was returning home and when he did he was so vague he might as well have said nothing. Isabel's response was to bottle up her emotions and convince herself she was an unwelcome cuckoo in an increasingly unsympathetic nest.

One afternoon, alone in the house, Isabel was fumbling down the side of the settee looking for a lost bracelet when she found a letter from her dad enclosing some money for her mum. In the letter her dad had given an address in Southampton. Bewildered, at times on the edge of tears, she struggled to keep her confusion to herself but she did, for days. She had to, for she had a plan. That weekend, without a word to anyone, Isabel took a train to a city that meant nothing to her and, she assumed, nothing to her father. But... why had he not come home from Aberdeen? What was he doing in Southampton? Her head was a mess of jumbled thoughts – which meant she was totally unprepared for what was to confront her.

Opening the front door, her dad wasn't so much surprised as aghast. He mouthed words that formed random, meaningless phrases that came together as incoherent sentences. But there was more. He was awkward. Different in a way that Isabel couldn't work out. Why didn't he seem pleased to see her? Why wasn't he inviting her in? Why was he blathering like an idiot?

"Dad, is that Carole?" A girl a few years younger than Isabel appeared in the hallway. Isabel stood motionless, barely able to comprehend what she had heard. She wanted to speak, say something, anything, but her voice was lost in her throat.

Over the next few minutes what became inexorably and distressingly clear to Isabel was that her world would never be the same again. Her dad had another family, another life. Yes he did work away but nowhere near as often and for as long as she had been led to believe. All those months apart, all that time alone desperately wanting her dad to come home, and he had chosen to be elsewhere. Not simply anywhere – he had wanted to be with his other 'wife' and children more than he had wanted to be with her. And yes, other *children*. She had three half-sisters. Somehow, irrationally it felt worse that they were girls. If they had been half-brothers she might not have felt so terribly rejected. Why was she not enough? And now, when he must have known how much she needed him, he had abandoned her. Isabel was inconsolable. Her head was spinning at a betrayal that surpassed any she thought her mother had committed. Yet in the midst of this turmoil she remained her father's daughter and all she wanted was to be held and reassured that all would be well. But at this point, possibly unwittingly, her father destroyed not only their relationship, but also, as time was to reveal, he also destroyed Isabel's self-confidence.

Hours had passed. No one, especially her dad, knew what more could be said, so exchanging glances with his 'wife' her father said: "Isabel, it's time you went home. I'll drive you." Go home! What was he talking about? Home is not about bricks and mortar, it's about relationships, affection, being safe, feeling it's where you belong. Where was her home? But her father had made his choice and never again was Isabel to feel worthy of being loved for who she was. Was her father bad? Probably not. Like many ordinary people he was simply flawed, but in a way that was to have awful repercussions for his daughter.

As for Isabel's mother, she had suspected for a long time that there was something unpleasant at the core of her marriage but it was only in the weeks before she had walked out that she had discovered for certain what her husband was up to. The truth was that Tony had been her friend, her loyal platonic confidant for years. Always there when she needed a shoulder, asking little of her and when the secret was uncovered it was to Tony that she went.

Over the next ten years, as she progressed through her teenage years and early twenties, Isabel's insecurities and mistrust led her from one doomed relationship to another. Until, that is, she met Nick. Twenty-six years old, she had found a man who wanted to care for her. A man she could trust, someone who took an interest in all she did. Eleven years of marriage followed, yet even having two sons and sharing much in common with Nick, she couldn't stop their relationship unravelling.

The problem for Nick was that, as Isabel relaxed into their marriage and fell in love with being a mother, she became more self-assured. She had opinions. She became more independent. But as she became more outgoing, Nick showed himself to be controlling to the point of suffocation. He always wanted to know where she was, what she was doing and, if she was longer than expected, why. If she did anything that Nick disagreed with he would sulk. He knew Isabel's weakness, her fragile confidence. It was too easy to undermine her with criticism, to sow self-doubt with sarcasm, and that is how her marriage unravelled. Ground down by her husband's words and controlling ways, she probably would never have had the courage to end their marriage but the rows were getting more frequent and the boys were being affected, especially Luke who would often come to his mother's defence protesting to his father that she had done nothing wrong.

So, as her mother had done years before, she left. She took the boys and, wracked with nerves and foreboding, she faced up to whatever Nick did to try to do get her and his sons to return. Her resources were depleted and her confidence was low, and Nick was as savage as he was determined. But she survived. She refused to be cowed.

Isabel drew strength knowing the boys needed her and she surprised herself with how well she rebuilt their lives. Yet while she knew it wasn't so, she once again felt terribly alone. Not lonely – how could she be with Luke and James? – but alone. Sometimes, she simply wanted to be held and loved for who she was and that meant being more than the boys' mum. And that's why she was happy coming home from the party. She had a man in her life once more.

The car accident came out of nowhere. One moment they were driving along, the next a car had accelerated out of a side road, skidded and careered into their car. The impact showered glass over her boyfriend and while he somehow kept control of the car despite the driver's door having caved in, the force of the impact propelled Isabel's head against the passenger door window. Dazed but certain she hadn't lost consciousness they were both taken to Accident & Emergency. More as a precaution than a necessity, Isabel had a CT brain scan. All was well. The wound on the side of her head above her left ear was stitched and dressed. She was told that if she felt drowsy or nauseous at any time during the next 48 hours she was to come back immediately, but she was fine other than for a pounding headache and stiff neck that lasted on and off for days. And that was it, life continued. The relationship with her boyfriend ended as so many had before, but this time she filled the void not with another partner but having discovered a fascination for computing. She enrolled as a part-time student studying computer science to degree level, while still working as a legal assistant. As if being a full-time mother to two growing boys was not demanding enough!

Then around 18 months ago she first noticed the signs that were soon to cause her such worry. Lapses of concentration, forgetting where she'd put things, the boys asking what's for dinner and she being as clueless as them because she hadn't given dinner a thought. Nothing major, but this was simply not who she was. Isabel was diligent and organised, not chaotic and unreliable. Initially she thought she was stressed, and that was her doctor's opinion. But several weeks later her tutor waited for her one evening to say her grades were showing a consistent trend from high Bs to Cs, and she already knew that at work she was feeling more and more out of control. Isabel sensed there was something seriously wrong. Again her GP thought it was stress, and given how busy and at times frenetic her life could be this was not surprising. But Isabel disagreed. She had known stress and worry and this felt different.

As the months passed Isabel found it took more and more effort and concentration to do the everyday things at home let alone manage her workload and keep up with her college work. Each day she felt more and more exhausted. At times she would just cry, not because she felt depressed but out of sheer frustration. "What's wrong with me?" But she had no answer. As life became more difficult it dawned on Isabel that some of the problems she was having weren't solely arising because she was struggling with her memory. She wasn't simply more absent-minded, she actually felt less intelligent. While for some time she had had a problem forgetting where things were, she now found herself on occasions actually not knowing what things were! And then there was her problem with numbers – on many occasions they literally didn't add up. She would struggle to make sense of her credit card statement and telephone bill, and in the supermarket she often found it impossible to work out how much she was spending.

Sitting again in front of her GP it was clear to both of them that this was not the consequence of stress. Reviewing her records he felt that possibly her problems could be to do with the car accident and "that nasty bang on your head". And that's why she found herself coming to see me. As Isabel recounted her story I was listening but also carrying out a neuropsychological examination. This is always how I favour working. While formal assessments reveal a lot, giving people a chance to talk not only provides you with an understanding of who they are it also gives you an opportunity to pick up subtle problems with memory, speech and thinking during conversation that an examination may miss. Tripping up over a word, losing concentration while talking, being unable to express a point of view or describe an event can jar because such errors interrupt the flow of conversation, and because they are unexpected they are even more noticeable. (Just as a man, still working as a senior executive yet within months of being diagnosed with Alzheimer's disease, said when talking to me about his daughter who had been engaged for five years: "I don't think she'll ever get married. She keeps putting it *away*, putting it *away*.")

Isabel told me about her forgetfulness and her problem with numbers, and how she just didn't feel intelligent anymore. Then she told me that, strangely, she would often ignore people standing to her left as if she didn't know they were there. On occasions she had been startled when someone seemed to have magically appeared in front of her because she had failed to see them coming towards her from her left. And why was it that she kept falling out with friends and family? Not only would she innocently say the wrong thing or appear unsympathetic, she was no longer able to simply chat and laugh. "You know, sometimes it feels as if I've lost my sense of humour.

With the examination completed and having met with Isabel on four occasions, nothing made sense. Her story, the problems she described, my examination, the test results had revealed a host of impairments and many not typical of a left-side temporal lobe lesion, the site of her head injury. To a greater or lesser extent Isabel had problems with a spread of deficits more associated with generalised brain lesions across both hemispheres, not a localised brain injury. There was no alternative but to request an MRI scan.

Sitting with Isabel I needed to know more, for I now suspected she had not told me everything. She at first insisted she had left nothing unsaid but I just didn't believe her. Not because I'd had a flash of insight or even that astute forensic analysis on my part had exposed an inconsistency in her story – it was because the MRI scan, more sensitive than a CT scan, had shown multiple tiny lesions scattered across her brain. Lesions that were years old and consistent with repeated blows. How had these been sustained? Had anyone beaten you, I asked? No, Isabel replied. But her monosyllabic response was simply a prelude. She dissolved into tears as she described not beatings, but violent shaking, at the hands of Nick. Twice to a point where she had lost consciousness. Their marriage had collapsed not because of the arguments but because of years of sustained physical abuse. If Nick didn't get his way, if she did something he didn't want her to, or maybe contradicted him in front of friends, later he would shout, swear and then he would simply lose it but in a way that left her in no doubt that he knew exactly what he was doing. He didn't beat her because he knew that would have left marks that would have had to be explained or, possibly worse for him, evidence that Isabel could have used against him. Instead he maliciously shook her as you would a rag doll. Not a mark could be seen, but internally her brain was vibrating and rebounding violently within her skull causing what are called coup and contrecoup injuries. As time passed these small bleeds and areas of damaged tissue had aggregated. What would initially have been years of degeneration with no clinical signs was now resulting in the problems of memory, intelligence and functioning Isabel was struggling to live with.

Unearthing the unpalatable reason for Isabel's difficulties could do nothing to redress what had happened. Yet with knowledge her desperation dissipated. It was as if knowing took away her greatest fear, that of not knowing. This was another legacy from her childhood. Stoically Isabel insisted she did not wish to revisit what was for her was a closed chapter, although clearly it was not. But I understood what she meant. There was nothing to be gained from confronting Nick, going over old ground, opening up wounds that were healing and, as she said, bringing him back into her life. Instead we agreed to move on from the position that 'life is not fair and it never will be' to 'let's concentrate on what can be done to make things better'.

Her life needed to be less cluttered, more organised. Priorities would need to be set in place without guilt even if that meant commitments had to be parked up to be revisited later. Tough decisions were needed. The first was her studies had to be postponed. For Isabel, her boys would always come first and that meant being a responsible and able parent, which meant keeping her job. However, helping Isabel was not solely about removing stress and streamlining her life; she needed strategies that would help her remember and be less error prone. So she became an avid list maker. Jobs to do, reminders of jobs done. She hit on the idea of not putting things away because then she would have to remember where she'd put them and, if she couldn't, she would waste time searching, getting more and more frustrated in the process. Instead her home began to resemble a supermarket with much of what she bought laid out seemingly on display on kitchen units, tables and even on the stairs ("I'm always up and down so it's a great place to spot things"). Her boys were mystified as to how all this untidiness was in some way making their mum's life easier but, as I said to them, what is clutter to one person is another's solution to not being able to remember.

In the midst of all she was doing to help herself she received wonderful support from her employers. She was hugely grateful to them for not only did they say she could work flexible hours, they also suggested she could work more from home if that would help. Their understanding was fostered by Isabel working for the firm of solicitors who had handled her divorce and when she confided why she was now finding life so difficult her boss could not have been more compassionate. She had suspected at the time of the divorce proceedings that Isabel had been abused.

With her life easier to manage, Isabel became more confident, her mood improved and each day she felt more optimistic. Even when she said her lists were no longer as helpful as they had been she was not despairing but instead she wanted a solution. I said it wasn't the lists that were the problem it was their location. Placing them on tables or on the arms of chairs meant they were not visible enough, so why not stick them on doors instead. She could then read them as she walked around the house rather than having to remember to walk over to a table to see what she had written and only then know what she needed to do. She took my advice and again Isabel got on with her life. But I was troubled. Why was remembering to check her lists now so difficult for her? Months earlier she had used her lists as a springboard to getting back on top of things, but now…

When I saw Isabel next I repeated a cognitive screening test I'd administered months earlier. She had dropped three points. I requested a repeat MRI scan. The results were what I feared. Not only was her brain more damaged, the changes were now typical of Alzheimer's disease. And this was to be her journey's end.

Isabel accepted the diagnosis with remarkable

resilience. She was determined to do all she could to delay what she knew would be the outcome. She would be sensible, even imaginative when facing the inevitable failings and difficulties that would come to dominate her daily life. "Remember," she said, wistfully smiling at her choice of word, "I've not only got myself to think about." Yet sometimes resilience and sheer force of will are not enough, and tragically Isabel's demise turned out to be extraordinarily rapid. In less than two years such was her inability to care for herself, let alone her sons, she entered a care home. She arrived dependent, disoriented and in many ways thankfully oblivious to the fact that a man had re-entered her life – for who was better placed to tell the nurses and care assistants what she needed, liked and disliked than her ex-husband? Nick was again in control.

TWO

Dashed expectations

Fate can be cruel. Jimmy was only 64 years old when he was diagnosed with dementia, probably Alzheimer's disease – eight months before he was due to retire. This was a time he and Cathy had not just been looking forward to, but had been budgeting for and planning for over two years. During those two years they had celebrated a new anniversary, marking the day the house had become theirs. Mortgage free at long last meant that, with their children settled, they could save for Jimmy's retirement and then live life to the full. For this couple this meant travel. A map of the world was pinned on the inside of their bathroom door. Red pins highlighted places abroad they had already visited, all in Europe except the one that was placed on the west coast of Canada, their one and only far-flung holiday. The blue pins dotted across the world were the exotic and adventurous places they were going to visit. And there were many, many pins. Dreams became animated conversations; thoughts ceased to be private wishes and became shared anticipation. They were going places!

With hindsight it was possibly three years before that awful day with the consultant that Cathy had her suspicions that things with Jimmy were not quite right. But how many times each month are you entitled to mislay your keys or forget what you were going to do next? Is three times in a month normal? No one's memory is perfect, and who hasn't got 101 things on their mind, or isn't distracted by the stresses of everyday life? If someone said four times, is that worrying? Or perhaps only twice a month? How was Cathy expected to know that something was seriously wrong with her husband?

She came to think that Jimmy's more casual, lack-adaisical approach to life was something to do with the euphoria he felt having paid off the mortgage because this had become so important to him. Weighed down by a job he no longer enjoyed, his work days were dismal. His company had been taken over a few years earlier, new faces had appeared, friends and good colleagues had gone, things were different and expectations were greater. "Jimmy, we need to be smart and lean in all we do. Shed old ways of thinking. Anything is now possible." Extraordinary results were anticipated. "Jimmy, we need you to be an outstanding leader. We need you to exceed expectations." Heaven help us, Jimmy thought. Once he asked to be considered for voluntary redundancy, but this was not possible. While it was clear he didn't quite fit, his was the legacy intelligence the business still needed. A year later he asked for early retirement. The answer was the same. So Jimmy worked to pay off the mortgage. A milestone to be passed, after which he and Cathy would reap the rewards.

At first Jimmy's absent-mindedness was amusing but as time passed Cathy, despite her best efforts, found herself becoming more irritated with her husband and on several occasions perplexed by his memory lapses. But what troubled Cathy most of all was how Jimmy's language had become less colourful. It was matter-of-fact, with little detail, just the bare bones of what needed to be said. He also didn't chat as he once did, while sometimes he had difficulty holding on to what was being said. "What was I saying?" became his catchphrase. Then one day Jimmy walked into the kitchen and said, "Cathy, why are there different coloured pins on that map in the bathroom?" In that moment Cathy's world collapsed. This was the day Cathy knew her life, their life together was not going to be as they had hoped. Nor was it going to remain as it was.

At work Jimmy had become more solitary, less engaging. His work had suffered but his loyal team had sheltered him, taking on more and more, correcting his mistakes and covering for him when he was late or he forgot a deadline. But there came a point when it was clear to all that Jimmy was badly under-performing. Unbeknown to him, a decision was taken to offer him what he had yearned for, early retirement, but before he could be told he took a day off to attend his memory assessment appointment with the consultant.

Early retirement happened a month later and Cathy and Jimmy's life was transformed, yet in a most surprising way. Not only did life get better, Jimmy got better. Jimmy's family and friends knew he had been unhappy at work for years but what only he knew was the degree to which he had been living with anxiety and stress in those final months. Relying on his fading intellectual powers and his fragile memory had become an increasingly precarious pursuit. Now that was all behind him and, as layers of stress were removed, not only did Jimmy's mood improve, so did his powers of concentration. No longer was he fretting and distracted. This meant his ability to remember improved, and unsurprisingly so did his willingness to chat. Of course such improvement was to be temporary for decline was inevitable, but this was a honeymoon to enjoy.

Yet Jimmy's relief at having left work was only one reason for the transformation; the other was Cathy, who was a truly remarkable woman. Jimmy was doing wonderfully well but in terms of what their life was to be like now and in the months ahead Cathy took the lead. They weren't going to dwell on the dreadful diagnosis. No, it was going on the back-burner, not because it was too awful to contemplate, but because they were not going to let it get in the way of them living life to the full. True, they were not going to have the retirement they had hoped for – but this was not a time for despair. Instead there were places to visit, moments to spend with children and grandchildren, friends to be with, even new friends to make. But also fences to mend, because in the grand scheme of things, did those misunderstandings from years past really matter? And this is how life turned out.

For nearly two years they both lived better with dementia than they could have imagined. Positive denial served them well. They did many things, went to many places, and enjoyed the company of people from near and far. All at a fast pace because time was of the essence. Holidays to exotic places didn't happen, for Cathy knew (even if Jimmy didn't) that these would be too over-whelming. A Mediterranean cruise and another around the Norwegian fjords were pearls of delight that brought not only joy but a real sense that if dementia was not being beaten it had retreated behind their determination to get on with their lives and do all that was possible to get close to their dreams.

There weren't many days that passed them by. Cathy even revelled in the irony that during the best of times with friends or when simply out and about she would forget Jimmy had dementia. But as they approached the second anniversary of that terrible day when they had sat opposite the consultant and Cathy's fears were confirmed, dark clouds had appeared on the horizon.

I had been seeing Cathy and Jimmy for routine monitoring, in the beginning every two months, and then as they revealed how well they were doing, every four months. How could I do otherwise? Can discharging a person after a diagnosis of dementia ever be the right thing to do? How can one discharge a person with a degenerative disease that is not only destined to get worse but, as they progressively deteriorate, the inevitability is they will become less aware of the troubles they face and the risks they run? As they unknowingly take a path toward an absence of insight, their condition ceases to be a private affair and embraces the lives of others, who themselves are on a journey from being a husband or wife, son or daughter to finding themselves first bemused spectators, then supporters, before their relationship finally becomes one of carer. And as their caring role becomes all embracing they are not the ones best placed to judge when enough is enough. To be a caring partner can be compared to being the parent of a young child. You don't see your children grow for you are too close, too inextricably enmeshed in their daily lives. It is only at times of deliberate reflection, or after time spent apart that you appreciate how they've grown; how they've changed. This is what it's like to be a carer.

Probably not week on week, but more likely month on month carers take on more and more, a little more assistance here, a touch more watchfulness there, ignorant of the fact that they are insidiously becoming ground down and worn out by their caring responsibilities. In other words they are drifting toward stress and strain with a sense that this is simply how things are. Meanwhile in an office somewhere there is a social worker or nurse prepared to accept a call for help that is never made or, if it is, it's only when the cusp of crisis has been reached.

Sitting next to me Cathy told me she was starting to despair. She talked about finding it difficult to cope whereas before she seemed to be taking everything in her stride. She didn't know how much longer she could go on. She said there were arguments, and once she thought Jimmy was going to hit her. At times he didn't even seem like her husband. He would never have done this or that, and nor would he have said such things before. "What's happening, am I losing him? Why does it feel so different?"

Cathy and Jimmy had done well but time had moved

on. As for everyone living with Alzheimer's disease, Jimmy's dementia was remorseless. Nowadays he didn't always recall why things were happening or what was expected of him. He would get in a muddle in the midst of doing something. He didn't find it easy to explain himself. Jimmy as a person had not changed but for him his life had. His world, once understood, was no longer. Frustrations came thick and fast and he was struggling.

I suggested that, in the same way that her husband's dementia had changed, it was time for Cathy to change how she related to Jimmy if she was going to continue to do the right thing not just for her husband, but for herself as well. Positive denial had held them both in good stead, but now it was time for dementia to come to the forefront of Cathy's thinking and for her to engage in positive acceptance. Not because this was the end but because she needed to acknowledge the savagery dementia was exercising on Jimmy's intellectual powers and build this into her plan for a life that could still be lived well. Their life together was not over, but flexibility and a different way of managing was now required. From now on it wouldn't matter if there were days that passed them by. There were going to be no more 'musts' or 'shoulds'. No more rigid timetables of 'things to do'. Things would all get done – eventually. It wouldn't matter if they were running late, or today was a day they might let friends down because Jimmy was not at his best. Friends would understand. Nor would it matter if Jimmy looked a little bit ragged around the edges. Good care is not measured by flawless appearances.

Cathy listened, learnt some lessons and within weeks

this formidable woman had once more set their life on an even keel and Jimmy was once more Jimmy. Yes, life was less predictable and at times it could be a touch chaotic, but it was good nevertheless. And as the harsh words and confrontations of the recent past faded from her memory, it proved a price worth paying. Yet if I had not been there for them, accompanying Cathy and Jimmy on their unfolding journey, the likelihood would have been that Cathy would have continued to do her best, not understanding that change was needed and eventually, and to her inexplicably, she would have found herself at breaking point. And when she could no longer carry on she would have found herself sitting before her GP pleading for something to be done. An antipsychotic to take the edge off Jimmy's anger? Possibly. Attendance at a day centre to give Cathy a break? More than likely. Or even a hospital admission for assessment. Maybe. All extreme consequences of abandoning a couple to their own devices until the point of crisis. In other words until their needs had become 'complex'.

THREE

If only...

At 11 years of age, did it matter that Lucy's parents had decided her bicycle would not be a new one? If truth be told it always had but now, 60 years on and living with early Alzheimer's disease, it unquestionably did.

Sitting opposite me in her comfortable yet meticulously tidy lounge she could not conceal her anxieties. But did anxiety come even close to describing what she was feeling? Dread, panic, terror were more apposite words to describe her emotional turmoil. As we talked, the same thought kept going round and round my mind, "I've never been with a more frightened patient."

The referral letter from her GP did not do justice to what needed to be addressed. It said Lucy was struggling to regain control of her life following her diagnosis of probable Alzheimer's disease nearly a year ago. Might I be able to help with some advice? 'Poss memory aids?' This is not an unusual request or need. As dementia emerges, concentration is difficult and a person's capacity to retain what they've been told or what they intend to do is rendered easier said than done. They may talk about feeling as if life is less and less under their control. Things seem to happen, or not happen, for reasons they cannot understand. Frustration, dismay and loss of confidence fill the void left by not knowing. Introducing memory aids and routines can help acquaint a person with what's been done and what still needs to be done.

Lucy's diagnosis had been very early in the disease process. As I got to know her I understood why. With no intention to judge, although others in her life had not been as understanding or tolerant, Lucy was a 'control freak'. She needed to know, for with knowledge comes the power to control all around you. This is how she had lived her life. Her marriage had ended within two years, and friends could be counted on the fingers of one hand – and that was a generous estimate. She would fall out with them for no other reason than they had decided what they were going to do on, say, an evening out. It didn't matter that Lucy might have suggested the same, the mere fact she hadn't made the decision or been consulted was enough for her to disagree or say 'okay' but then be sullen, obstructive and resentful. Whatever I might do to try to help Lucy, this was never going to be just about memory aids and diaries.

Lucy was a middle child, one of three sisters, and she had never felt special. She herself described it as middle child syndrome. Everything that is done with the eldest is new, extraordinary and a wonder, while the youngest is destined to remain the 'baby' of the family, to be spoilt and indulged. It is rarely the same when you are the middle child. And this is how it was for Lucy. She felt squeezed out of her parents' affection. Was this true? I doubt it, but all that mattered was this is how it felt for Lucy. At her core she felt unremarkable. Average, unexceptional and most certainly not adored. So she would try harder, do more, but nothing changed, probably because as a young child the understanding she brought to her family relationships, the actions of her parents and siblings, and probably her life in general, was wrong.

It is for some of us a tragedy that 'the child is parent to the adult'. We develop an appreciation of who we are that is founded on our observations and interpretations of events and experiences while a naive young child. A time when, without the capacity for empathy, we are incapable of truly appreciating the actions of others, the light and shade of who they are and what they do. Hence our understanding of how things are may be far removed from how they actually are. Yet this isn't understood, and beliefs, attitudes and ways of feeling, profound and unerring, are laid down to influence who we will become. As adults this means we can unwittingly judge ourselves and others by listening to our inner child. And Lucy did.

When Lucy was nine her eldest sister passed the entrance examination to the grammar school and her parents gave her a brand new bicycle as a reward for all her hard work. A shining, glorious testimony to her success. When her youngest sister passed the entrance exam she too received a new bicycle. When Lucy passed the entrance examination to the grammar school she was given her older sister's bicycle as a 'hand-me-down'. A bicycle no longer needed or wanted by her sister. Is this all she and her efforts were worth? Was she really so unworthy? Or, instead, was it more to do with these being tough times for her parents who were not wealthy and who couldn't afford to buy Lucy a new bicycle at this time. After all, there were less than two years between Lucy and her elder sister, and Marjorie had looked after the bicycle so it looked nearly new. It would do. By contrast, when her younger sister passed the entrance exam three more years had passed and there was no way the bicycle could ever be said to be 'as good as new'. So Barbara got a new bicycle. Common sense reigned. Hard times were managed. Or were her parents' actions proof that Lucy wasn't special? Young Lucy *knew* it was the latter.

If Lucy could not trust her parents to do right by her then who could she trust? Not her elder sister, as events were to show, although if only she had asked if she could borrow her dress things might have been different. But, maybe believing the answer would be no, because it was one of Marjorie's favourites, she didn't. She was 14 and in love. Adored at last, by her first boyfriend. So far they had only walked, talked and secretly held hands but this was to be their first real date. A Saturday night out at the cinema. Lucy felt good as she caught a glimpse of herself in the shop window. She looked quite grown up and her boyfriend's eyes conveyed how he felt. She was special.

Yet at that moment of joy how was she to know that Marjorie and her friends were going to see the same film, at the same cinema, at the same time? As Lucy and her boyfriend walked to the end of the queue she came face to face with her sister. Marjorie was merciless. She humiliated Lucy in front of not only her boyfriend but everyone else who heard her poisonous attack. In floods of tears, Lucy literally ran home and swore to herself that never again would she trust or rely on anyone to treat her with kindness or generosity. Even though she did not have a high opinion of herself, there had always been a steeliness about Lucy and from now on she decided if she was to have the life she deserved then it would be down to her, nobody else. From now on she would take control.

Unfortunately, in her desperate bid for independence, when just 19 she made the error of getting married to an army corporal, for hers was a military town and on a Saturday night out it was soldiers you met. Unsurprisingly the marriage was destined to fail, for her need to be in control did not sit well with a man who was used to his words being obeyed. Even though he was only a few years older than Lucy he was from different world, a world where women knew their place and husbands were the decision-makers.

Divorced and mistrusting of others, her controlling ways led her down many emotional cul de sacs. Friendships ended, relationships failed and at times Lucy felt she was in a bottomless, hopeless, lonely rut. She often imagined what it might be like to feel special, yet in reality she was emotionally walled off, invariably a spectator on her own life, but at least it was her life and she could live with the consequences. However, when she was in her late 30s she realised she would not cope well with old age.

Her father was seriously ill with chronic obstructive pulmonary disease and was very frail. With him confined to his bed, Lucy's mother was his full-time carer. Lucy would visit to give her moral support rather than to do anything practical. One day while chatting with her mother their conversation was interrupted by a loud banging on the ceiling. "What's that, Mum?" a somewhat startled Lucy asked. "It's just your father," she said, and she carried on talking to Lucy. Moments later the banging started again. "Him and his bloody walking stick," her mother muttered as she poured a cup of tea for herself. Lucy couldn't recall whether it was after the fourth, fifth banging or "it might have been the tenth time" she said, "Mum, aren't you going to do something? You can't just ignore him."

"I'm not ignoring him. I'll go upstairs in a minute, but I'm not going to be at his beck and call." From that point Lucy's dread of old age began, a fear which would one day morph into a profound terror of dying. Not death, but dying, for she had realised that when you are aged, sick and frail you are no longer in control of what happens to you – others are. Whether the decisions be big or small you are unlikely to have the final say. Others, whether it be malevolently or benevolently (and for Lucy motivation did not matter), would determine your fate.

While she could not avoid old age and eventual death she could do all that was possible to stay well and delay the onset of infirmity. She became preoccupied with her health to the point that her GP entered into her medical records when she was 47 years old '*Pt. requesting full health assessment. Told not poss. on NHS. Hypochondriacal ++*'. Lucy even became terrified she would be pronounced dead when she was in fact deeply asleep or unconscious and she would be buried alive. For a time she became preoccupied with the Lazarus syndrome where people have been pronounced clinically dead but come back to life.

Unsurprisingly such extreme fears resulted in Lucy being referred for psychological therapy, with little benefit. To be in control was everything to her. She could not relinquish her conviction that only she could act in her own best interests. To believe otherwise was to risk being disappointed, let down and taken advantage of. These were immutable engrained beliefs. Lucy ended up hoping that as she grew older common sense would prevail and her irrational fears would dissipate, that she would accept the reality of the human condition and confront failing health with resignation if not equanimity. Alas this was not to happen.

Even before she received the diagnosis of probable Alzheimer's disease such was her hypochondria Lucy had convinced herself that she had dementia. Her GP was reassuring, saying she was only 70, which was a relatively young age to be diagnosed with dementia, and while she was protesting her memory was poor and concentrating was difficult he couldn't detect anything wrong – and, if truth be told, her fears and worries were over minor, incidental memory lapses. This was all true: Lucy admitted she was talking about the fine details of her life and agreed that to most people she was fretting unnecessarily. But she knew something was wrong, for she prided herself on knowing all that was happening around her. Remembering was at the heart of her psychological DNA because knowledge gave her the information and opportunity she needed to control her life. Lucy insisted she be referred to the local memory assessment service.

The interview with the consultant psychiatrist went well, at least from his perspective. All was fine. They had talked at length. A full history had been taken. Lucy had talked about her day-to-day life and she had described her difficulties. She talked eloquently with good recall and after having been equally impressive answering the test questions that were exploring her ability to remember and reason, the consultant reassured her that in all likelihood everything was fine. Again Lucy refused to accept this. The consultant briskly reiterated that it was exceedingly unlikely she had dementia, and if she stopped worrying her memory would improve. 'Stress not helping' was scribbled in the notes. "But aren't there more tests you can do? Ones that are more, I don't know, more sophisticated?" The consultant, like his GP colleague relented, and while he did not agree to a brain scan he referred Lucy to a neuropsychologist.

The neuropsychologist was not so certain all was well. She agreed that, in someone with a lifelong heightened awareness of their memory performance, change may be detected by that person unusually early. The neuropsychological examination was inconclusive but the in-depth assessment of Lucy's memory, attention, executive function, perception and language had revealed subtle failings that couldn't be simply be dismissed. Lucy was offered another appointment... in six months.

Those months were horrendous for Lucy. She was living with not knowing. She felt abandoned but in her rational, calmer moments she appreciated that time needed to pass before she could have a repeat examination. To cope she decided to take matters into her own hands. She went on the internet; she rummaged the shelves of the local library; she eavesdropped on conversations at the Women's Institute. Everything convinced her she had dementia. This time her morbid misgivings would be proved right.

The second examination, while not producing a set of crisp and definitive test results, did now suggest a diagnosis of dementia typical of Alzheimer's disease. Her psychological watchfulness had resulted in her once more 'knowing'. However, while knowledge had previously given Lucy an all-important sense of being in control, this was never going to be the way now. The news emotionally derailed her.

Dementia is among the most feared conditions associated with getting older, resonating not only with decline and dependency, but stigma too (Batsch & Mittelman 2012). For Lucy her fear knew no limits. She was now in a living nightmare, not solely because she knew what dementia intended for her (dementia comes from the Latin *demens* meaning 'out of one's mind') but because she knew that as her intellectual frailty became all consuming others would step in to tell her what to do, when to do it and with whom she would do it. As an independent person with a mind of her own she would cease to exist and the prospect filled her with uncontrollable horror. This is what the referral to me was actually about. Memory aids were never going to touch the sides of Lucy's existential crisis.

However, I decided to start with some basic tips because there was a need for Lucy to reclaim a degree of confidence and a sense of autonomy. Her absentmindedness was fuelling her fears for the future and she was was spiralling out of control. We talked about how routines, especially established ones, a well-ordered life and lists would provide predictability and a reassuring safety-net, helping her to feel more in control. She appreciated the common sense in what I was saying yet she didn't accept my advice without first perusing the internet and telling me two weeks later that she thought these were useful suggestions and worth trying! Even at the level of practical support, Lucy had to share the decision-making. For this I will always be grateful to Lucy, for thereafter I always felt I was a better practitioner when helping people with early dementia, seeing my work more as a partnership, appreciating that they were the true experts when it came to knowing what was right for them and what was not.

Lucy agreed that her world had to shrink. The more she had to remember, the more there was to forget. The more she did, the more she needed to know and hence the more she would feel the stress of not knowing. We talked about what was most important to her and hence what she didn't want to forsake. That meant still going to the Women's Institute and enjoying the talks and activities, but relinquishing the position of branch secretary. She had never liked shopping so why not sit in front of her personal computer with a list and do her food shopping online? Click on what she wanted, a red tick against the item on her list and, when it was delivered, cross it off as each item was unpacked and put away.

She enjoyed the cinema and that didn't have to stop because it was only a short walk from where she lived.

Coach trips? Maybe not, for there was always much to organise, too much that was novel, people to meet who she didn't know. Did she really want names to recall and conversations to have with the risk that she might lose the thread and repeat herself?

So her world contracted and within her more cloistered existence, with its comforting routines, she felt more in control. Not because her concentration and memory had improved but because there was less to remember, as there was now less she needed to know.

However, could we do more? Might it be possible for Lucy to learn to trust others, so there could be people she could confide in and rely on? Not someone like me who she might see for an hour or so once a fortnight, but people who could be there for her – and she for them – in her daily life. She had always mistrusted the motives of others, believing they were driven by their own self-interests, but might it be possible to undo this near lifetime inability to trust?

Counselling people with dementia is uncommon but more and more there is evidence that it can help (Cheston & Jones 2009). Even though she wasn't keen, Lucy acquiesced and I introduced her to a group of people all diagnosed with early dementia, a couple nearly 20 years younger than her, the others around her own age. Doreen, Tim, Ken, Charles, Gordon and Paddy had come together in a counselling group organised by a colleague. England's National Dementia Strategy (2009) emphasised the need for early diagnosis and those, like Lucy, who receive one will not only have insight into their cognitive failings but they will also appreciate the implications of that diagnosis.

The group explored feelings of insecurity, hopelessness, dependency and loss of control, the very issues Lucy was struggling with. All who were attending the group said they were benefiting from the advice and guidance they received, encouraging them to see the benefits of taking each day at a time, not dwelling on what you can't do but focusing instead on what you can and not losing perspective if you forgot, failed or fell short. Critically they felt better because they could talk to each other and share their worries. It was this therapeutic camaraderie that I wanted to draw Lucy into. They met outside the group; they would call each other, offer solutions and give each other the opportunity to talk. If Lucy could become part of this group she would see that none had a self-serving agenda. Whether it be Paddy, Tim or any of the others, all had found themselves in a place they would never have wished to have been, but now they were they were there for each other, and as they helped one another it made them feel better about themselves. Here was evidence that despite their memory and intellectual struggles they were in no way useless with nothing to offer.

Lucy agreed to attend six sessions. On the first couple of occasions she was quiet, even withdrawn, but after that, bit by bit, she opened up. As she did, Lucy found these were people just like her, who, while not having the same intense need as she did to be in control of everything and everybody, also shared many of her fears. In a way "it was as if we were as one. I've never felt that way. From time to time I didn't even have to ask if we were worrying about the same things. I knew we were.

Sometimes I'd get home and all I wanted to do was to ring one of them". Lucy never mentioned 'trust' for that probably remained a word that was best left unspoken but that's what she was feeling. And she flourished.

Her world was more limited, her horizons constrained, but within this world she had found compassion and people she could count on, and for many months her mood lifted. She felt better not solely because she had found people who were there for her but because she was also a helping hand to them, strangers who had now become her friends. Friendships formed within the midst of human misfortune.

Lucy was living if not well; she was living better with dementia than she could have anticipated. This was a huge achievement for her but inwardly I knew one day there would be an inevitable outcome for she was destined to be her own worst enemy.

Lucy had faith in her new-found friends but nothing had changed when it came to listening to her family, let alone professionals. She lost confidence in me when I advised she needed to inform the licensing authority that she was no longer safe to drive. "It's not that you can't drive, Lucy, but I'm concerned about your judgement and how well you're anticipating risk and hazards. If you don't report your condition and you have an accident your car insurance won't be valid." She railed against this as she knew it would seriously undermine her independence, and that would mean losing more control of her life.

Three years passed and Lucy entered the autumn of her dementia. Her new-found friendships were no more; most had been forgotten. Her life and times were now very different. But she remained the Lucy of old. There was to be no Lasting Power of Attorney for she was never going to relinquish control over her affairs. As her daily living skills deteriorated she wouldn't contemplate having a home care worker to support her. She wasn't going to have her home turned into a care setting, "I'm not going to be told by a stranger who [sic] I can and can't do in my own house." And as it became evident that she was becoming more and more vulnerable, her sisters tried to persuade her to move somewhere where there would always be someone to help and make sure all was well, but with no success. And then Lucy fell. She tore her ankle ligaments and the weeks she spent in hospital recovering were the testimonial to her future. Disoriented, bewildered but always true to herself, Lucy resisted efforts to assist her, assistance often dictated by routines, provided by nurses who barely knew her. She would often refuse to eat. She was unwilling to be accompanied to the toilet. And as for bathing, such intimacy was not to be shared.

There was never any prospect that Lucy would be discharged home to live alone. Eleven weeks after the fall Lucy moved into a care home. While that was the objective reality who knows what it meant to Lucy? Yet whatever the place meant to her it was not where she wanted to be. Emotionally she was again in turmoil. Resistive, agitated, pacing the corridors, pulling on door handles, calling out, she was not at peace. Finding herself confined, being cared for but equally being told what to do, invariably 'now', how could it have turned out any other way? Her family rarely visited, no friends came, carers struggled to 'manage' her, many despaired, all saw her as the most difficult resident they had. You could not disagree, for her ways were challenging. Except I saw it differently. I saw a young girl who had never felt she mattered, a woman who had wanted to feel special, a person who could never trust others. If only her bicycle had been new.

FOUR

It was always about the children

In her kitchen, pouring a well-deserved glass of wine, Caroline reflected on another day at work. It had been a good day. Demanding, busy, but enjoyable nevertheless. Standing in front of a class of six-year-olds all bursting with energy and curiosity could be tiring, on some days exhausting, but there was always compensation. And by that Caroline didn't mean seeing young children learn, for that was why she was a teacher, a lifelong purpose she was passionate about. No, the compensation was the opportunity for fun and laughter. And today had been no exception. She smiled as she thought especially when... When what?

How strange! Caroline could not remember what she felt had been an extremely amusing incident. Inwardly she could feel the joy. She could sense the laughter. There was a vague recollection of smiling faces but no more. There was no context. Nothing upon which she could anchor her pleasurable feelings. Peculiar, but she was probably more tired than she had realised. For goodness' sake, it was after 7pm and she had only just got in. As usual, after lessons she had been chatting in the staff room. There was so much going on, and yet again she had volunteered to lead the next parent-teacher meeting. Well, she had been at the school for 16 years and everyone had so much confidence in her. But her usual after school conversations were not why she was so late home. No, that was because she had left her shopping behind in the staff room. Not that surprising, for she'd seized an opportunity to quickly pop out at lunchtime. Shopping during the day was out of the ordinary, so inadvertently leaving it behind was forgivable. Caroline didn't give it a second thought.

Sitting with me months later her absentmindedness was all she thought about. She was frightened, and as she spoke about her memory problems and stupid mistakes, sometimes amusing, often not, she cried uncontrollably. There was no doubt Caroline was struggling badly. Aged 51, divorced and living alone, her work meant everything to her, and that was where it was going very wrong. Her life at home was predictable and she coped. She knew where things were and what to do, but at work things were different. Caroline meticulously prepared her lessons but 30 small children could easily upset her best-laid plans and then she struggled. "I get in such a state. On a good day I just about get by. Most days I fail miserably." Caroline dissolved once more into tears.

She told me how hard it was to concentrate, how if distracted she couldn't remember what she had planned to say or do. "Do you know what it's like standing in front of a class of children, all gazing at you and you feeling blank? Not knowing what you are going to say? You want the ground to swallow you up." And then there was the noise, on occasions excruciating noise. "It can be anything. The children's voices, their laughter, even when they move their chairs, it's all too much. The noise just grates on me. It's wrong I know, but I get angry and I see their faces and…" Her voice tailed off as she started to cry again.

Neuropsychological examination revealed a picture typical of early Alzheimer's disease. Problems acquiring new learning (when asked to recall six photographs of everyday objects, Caroline could only remember two), with word-finding (known as the FAS test) and reasoning. While she did well on the similarities test which examines how items are alike, such as apple-banana, table-chair, the clock drawing test caused her more difficulty. She struggled to set the hands of the clock to '10 past 11', eventually saying, "I don't know what to do. 10 isn't right, is it?" Even though I had noticed on several occasions that she seemed poised to draw a hand to the 2, the 'dementia pull' always drew her back towards the 10.

I next saw Caroline three weeks later. A few days earlier she had been given a diagnosis after the results of the CT scan of brain had shown Alzheimer-type brain atrophy. "I'm only 51 and now I feel like an old woman," she told me. "What can I do?"

We talked about all the sensible things she might do. How she would benefit from having a routine. Never saying I'll do it in a minute, for she might forget what she intended to do. Instead do it right away. Write things down. Carry a notebook to keep track of important information such as what's been done, what needs to be done, phone numbers, names, ideas, appointments, her address, and directions home. Put sticky notes around the house with reminders. A place for everything, everything in its place. Yet despite her listening to all I advised I knew Caroline's dementia would be difficult for her to manage.

Caroline had taken the diagnosis badly and I was certain her intellectual state would now be affected by worries and anxieties, and probably depression, all conspiring to undermine her ability to concentrate and exaggerate her problems with remembering. She also lived alone, which meant she was going to be completely reliant on her own capacity to recall the guidance she'd been given. However, my greatest concern was to do with how long she could carry on teaching. This was where her soul was to be found. Everything she had told me had given me the impression that her life away from work was of secondary importance. She had friends and a social life but without a partner or children it was her work that gave her the belief that she mattered. It's where she felt confident and good about herself. Without her job I feared she would spiral downwards, yet supporting her at work would not be easy.

Dementia is an intellectual disability, one that progresses over years to a stage of severe deficits in memory, language and thought, but in the early years it is an irritating, frustrating and, depending on circumstances, embarrassing intellectual frailty. And as with all disabilities regardless of nature and origin, the person cannot be discarded. Instead they should be helped to be as able and productive as possible, to feel valued and not to be known solely for their weaknesses. To feel included and not marginalised in their communities – this includes the workplace.

When a person of working age is given a diagnosis of dementia it cannot be right that their disability immediately clouds our view of them, and thoughts of mistrust and liability are automatically in the air. Instead we need to ask what can be done to make the working environment more supportive. Can the working day become more predictable without the interference of competing stimulation, the distraction of background noise, or the pressure of inflexible deadlines? Might the work setting be uncluttered, yet rich in reminders and essential information? Once we start to think like this we can appreciate how we can support people who wish to work following a diagnosis of dementia. This will become a more pressing concern for society, especially in high income countries, as we address the needs of an ageing workforce, in particular workers aged between 65-74 as more and more governments raise the age of statutory retirement. This is a decade when there is a marked increase in the risk of dementia.

While I anticipate we can make great strides in re-designing work settings and occupations, will all jobs lend themselves to supportive interventions and designs? Will we be able to support doctors, bus drivers, electricians and teachers if they wish to remain at the sharp end of what they do? Probably not.

Caroline valiantly continued working for another two terms, but it all got too much for her. There was no more fun and laughter, and from the perspective of some parents not a lot of learning either. Caroline frequently lost control of her class as she attempted to teach from plans she could barely remember. Sometimes her conduct could be quite erratic, although this was as much to do with the emotional turmoil she was experiencing as it was to do with the progression of her dementia. She knew if she could just step back and give herself time to gather her thoughts she could do better but this just wasn't possible. Her headteacher was sympathetic – some of her lessons were taken off her and her administration workload was reduced, but everyone knew Caroline was still struggling. And so did Caroline.

She was not surprised when the headteacher asked to see her. The school day was over. The children respectfully said their goodbyes as they filed out of the classroom. Caroline saw the headteacher waiting in the corridor. They walked over to her office and when she saw the chair of governors sitting there also she knew what to expect. She was asked to take indefinite sick leave and during that time a severance package would be arranged. There were weak smiles, reassuring words spoken and supportive comments made but nothing could temper the chill in Caroline's heart as she now faced the end she had dreaded. Yet even though the outcome was as she feared, and it was probably for a time more tragic than she would have contemplated, in some ways it wasn't.

Caroline's most significant problem was her difficulty storing experiences that were ongoing or recent. Her memory for what she intended to do would also let her down. This is often referred to as a problem with short-term memory. Knowing she had to live with this every waking moment, it was easy to see how Caroline's problems at work had accumulated. Now her friends and ex-colleagues rallied around and during the months that followed her resignation she probably had a more active social life than ever before. Some even noticed how Caroline was happier and more relaxed, but what nobody could see, and only Caroline could appreciate, was that Alzheimer's disease was insidiously progressing toward greater intellectual ruin.

Every morning Caroline woke she had less and less recall of the previous day's events. She didn't dwell on this if for no other reason than that's not how a person with dementia lives life. Increasingly it is the immediate present that occupies them. They live in the midst of routines and automatic ways. They do not reflect and wonder "What did I do yesterday?". And if we are honest, nor do we unless we are prompted to do so by others or by our own intentional thought processes.

So on one unremarkable morning Caroline got out of bed and followed her routines. Who knows how long it took her to get ready for the day ahead, a day like any other, but now she was ready and her day began.

Sheila was pleased to see her, although somewhat surprised. Caroline was simply pleased to have arrived.

"Good morning, Sheila."

"A little late for good morning, Caroline, it's nearly half past one," replied Sheila, smiling broadly "but anyway how are you? It's been ages."

"Ages. Really?" Caroline looked quizzically at Sheila. "Why do you say that? But, if I don't know... I can't keep them waiting."

"Who have you come to see?"

"See? I haven't come to see anyone."

In just seconds Sheila's pleasure at seeing Caroline after all these months had turned into unease. "Caroline, what are you doing here?"

"The same as you Sheila. Just another day." And Caroline smiled.

The same as me? What do you mean Caroline?" And then, with a resigned sigh, Sheila said, "Caroline you don't work here any more."

Caroline just stood there as if appreciating something was wrong but having no idea what it could be. Sheila didn't know what to say. Or more accurately, what not to say. Aren't you supposed to agree with people with dementia who are confused? Here was Caroline standing in the staff room clearly thinking she had arrived at work.

As Alzheimer's disease progresses, the memory impairment that dominates the beginnings of the dementia evolves from an inability to remember what is happening, or just happened, to forgetting what was most recently remembered. For Caroline, as more and more recent memories are destroyed, when she wakes in the morning where would she go? To work, obviously. To her the experiences of recent months have not happened, or if they have they are so on the periphery of who she is and the reality of what she knows her life to be they warrant no reflection. Her life is her work. She cannot recall the generous gifts, kind words, tearful embraces and fond farewells. So when she wakes she goes to work. From our perspective she is confused, yet Caroline does not believe she has a job, she *knows* it, and this is her reality, the frame of reference for all she does.

As weeks passed her brothers became increasingly exasperated as they were telephoned again and again by the headteacher telling them that Caroline had once more arrived at school, convinced she'd come to teach, and she wouldn't leave.

As Ribot's Law (of retrograde amnesia) slowly and remorselessly exercised its effect, more and more of Caroline's experiences from her recent past disappeared but still she knew she needed to get to school. Sometimes she even went in the evening, for disorientation rendered the passing of time meaningless. No longer was Caroline described as happy and relaxed; now, on arriving at school, she could become distressed and agitated. At times she could be abusive. Those who knew her at least understood how she must have felt being prevented from walking into classrooms and being led away from perplexed children who were puzzled by her attempts at conversation. Nowadays Caroline's speech was sparse, repetitive, fragmented and replete with nonsense words known as neologisms.

Her desperate need to get to school represented complete conviction. And not just once a day. Having been brought home it was as if she looked around and said to herself "Why am I here?", and out she would go again. With her living by herself there was no one to keep a watchful eye on her. The strain on her family became immense. They were worried about how dangerous

Caroline's life had become, going out at all times of day and night even though she had never got lost, had always returned home and still possessed her road sense. Yet might tomorrow be the day her judgement of speed and distance let her down? Then there were the incidents at the school. The headteacher was understanding but the situation was unacceptable. It wasn't simply that her presence was disruptive, but her behaviour was causing parents to complain. One had already written to her local councillor voicing her concerns. Caroline's neighbours were alerted but what could they do? Caroline was immune to persuasion. School is where she had to be because that's where she was needed. And in truth that is where she needed to be. So all they could do was to contact one of her brothers to say "Caroline's gone out again". The cycle of stress and worry continued unabated.

Caroline's brothers talked about her living with one of them but neither Gary nor Dave could see how it could possibly work. They both had jobs, their wives worked. They had teenage children. Life was hectic, unpredictable and most days Caroline would still be alone, so how would the situation have been improved? Caroline would be just as determined to get to school even though she would no longer be living a 25-minute walk away. Instead she would have to negotiate several miles of unknown roads and unfamiliar high streets. No, it was impossible to contemplate. Caroline would be no safer and more secure living with one of them than she would be if she continued to live by herself. Having spoken to the social worker, there was only one option: Caroline needed to move into a care home, one that specialised in caring for younger people with dementia. Unfortunately that was to prove impossible.

Younger-onset dementia is typically defined as occurring before the age of 65 years and, because it is uncommon, accounts for probably only around 5 per cent of all cases of dementia. Specialist services and care homes are few and far between as Gary and Dave were to find out. Despite their best efforts, and their social worker did all she could, to find a care home that had experience of caring for younger people with dementia, the only one she found was more than 30 miles away and neither brother felt this was a good idea because both wanted to be able to visit regularly and often. They were frustrated and angry when offered no option other than to accept a care home for older people. The fact that Caroline was going to live alongside people whose average age was 83 years old did nothing to dispel their guilt.

Unsurprisingly Caroline didn't adjust well but this was less to do with the age of the other residents and more to do with Caroline knowing where she had to be, rather than knowing where she did not want to be. Now living behind a baffled front door, her days were intolerable. She would stand facing the door pleading, "I can't get out. I've got to go," and whenever she saw a passer-by she would bang on the windows desperately trying to attract their attention. A woman deteriorating with dementia, or a woman distressed beyond belief?

Samuel Smith House had a very good reputation and so Caroline's brothers were disappointed that their sister's anguish seemed greater than ever. They had been asked so many questions about what Caroline liked and disliked, her family and work life, her habits and routines, her worries and interests, they had hoped this would lead to Caroline enjoying a meaningful life in the home, but no, it didn't happen.

The home manager and Caroline's key worker nurse were sensitive to Caroline's confused need to be at school. They weren't surprised when Dave spoke of his sister's passion for teaching and how she used to come alive in front of her class. He and his brother had been asked to bring in possessions to personalise her room, along with any artefacts and mementoes from school which could help occupy her through the day. But this proved not to be so. Caroline would spend a few moments glancing at the books and school photos placed before her then she would head off to the front door pleading to leave. The home's activity coordinator felt a few mementoes were not enough to keep her occupied and so she went the extra mile and purchased exercise books, pencils, rulers and even a couple of teaching resources.

The table was resplendent with all you might expect to see on a teacher's desk. A small pile of books, a globe (Caroline had taught a bit of everything but geography was the subject she had enjoyed most), a pencil box, books 'to hand out', a photograph of her colleagues from school and, as a touch of humour, an apple. It was Caroline's desk. It resonated with nostalgia. Yet at best it absorbed Caroline for merely a few moments longer. She soon pushed her chair away from the table and walked into the hallway. Was it possible that 'the classroom' was prompting her need to leave for school and hence it was never going to be the way to occupy her for it simply triggered confusion and agitated her even more? This was possible, for it is naive to automatically assume that a passion, interest or routine from the past will lead to the person being engrossed and content. Instead it may prompt searching for 'the past' or possibly, for some, generate frustration because they can no longer perform as well as they once did. However, for Christine I felt the answer lay elsewhere.

Nowadays many care homes have created reminiscence rooms or 'nostalgia' destination points at hallway ends or in a nook somewhere. The admirable intention is to provide interest and give reason for residents to walk around the building. And as historical memories are best preserved in dementia, reminiscence features are meaningful, offering familiarity and hopefully provoking pleasurable emotional memories. So we may find a scullery from the 1950s with washing to be folded, washing-up to be put away and cupboards to be tidied. Similarly from the same era we may find beach scenes, pubs, cafes and cinemas all touched by the creativity of committed staff, and all expected to provide residents with occupation to help improve their mood. Yet the danger is that care homes are promoting neither occupation nor enjoyment but instead are transforming areas of the building into nothing more than social history museums. Rooms where historical artefacts are laid out and displayed.

Our lives are only fleetingly joyous and uplifted by things and places. Happiness comes from relationships and the joy of sharing. Caroline's thrill came from the smiles of children and the companionship of her colleagues. Teaching was her passion because of the children before her, not because of the items on her desk. At the end of the day she liked nothing more than chatting in the staff room with her fellow teachers. All this was missing. There was no conversation, no sharing, and no laughter. What had been provided was not wrong, it was just not enough.

Of course the desk had to remain, for the activity coordinator and Caroline's key worker had invested time and effort in creating a wonderfully personalised stage upon which Caroline could become engrossed. But now people needed to come onto that stage, carers who would sit with her and chat about the globe, look at the books and ask questions about her life as a teacher. And why not position the desk so it looked into the lounge giving the impression that the residents were her pupils. Fanciful? Possibly, but as we all know confusion is nearly always impervious to the reality of the world around – there was good reason why reality orientation when faced with confusion was called reality confrontation. How else could ideas of being at work be sustained when the surroundings of a care home are so different? Or when a man is certain his female care worker is his wife when their appearances share nothing in common? Or when searching for young children, an aged reflection in the mirror, the style of contemporary dress, the technology that abounds and the design of passing present-day cars fail to undermine a person's conviction that life is how they know it to be?

And so behind her desk Caroline sat. Not throughout the day, and not on all occasions, but for sufficient time for her need to leave the building for "Getting, going, going to school, my school" to have diminished. Life had become more tolerable, not in terms of staff feeling less pressured but because the fewer times Caroline tried to leave the more everyone knew she was now more content. Her life was better for living in the care home. This was most certainly the case at weekends because the activity coordinator was a marvel. She spoke to every member of staff, nearly all of whom were mothers or grandmothers, and she organised a rota. So who came to be sitting with or playing in front of a gratified Caroline on Saturdays and Sundays? None other than the staff team's own children and grandchildren. Or in Caroline's eyes, her fun-loving, amusing pupils. Once more her life felt right and at these times the end she feared was cast aside as once more she found herself where she needed to be.

PART II

A *question of diagnosis*

*"Diagnosis is not the end,
but the beginning of practice"*
– MARTIN H FISCHER

FIVE

The tale of two brothers

There was a knock on the door and James slowly entered. Accompanied by a nurse, he looked shambolic and bewildered. As his eyes surveyed the cluttered ward office I asked whether he'd like to sit down. There was no hint of acknowledgement. He stood in the middle of the room and then, in obvious mental disarray, he turned and headed back to the door. On reaching it he could not have been more perplexed. He simply didn't know what to do. His hands rotated in a ponderous, uncoordinated fashion and then, as if the effort was too great or simply just pointless, he stopped and stood motionless, facing what to us was the door – but who knows what it represented to James? The nurse walked over, opened the door and James shuffled out. He had not spoken a word.

His posture was aged but James was a youthful-looking 42-year-old man who had been on the psychiatric ward for months. Despite his gross mental and physical dilapidation he had no history of previous illnesses. On admission his physical examination had been normal. Infections had been excluded. He was not known to have had seizures. A raft of medications to calm and stabilise him had failed. There had not been a trace of recovery. At times his behaviour was bizarre and having read his notes and spoken to his psychiatrist his state of mind continued to baffle everyone. At times he was withdrawn and uncommunicative; at other times he was anxious and appeared to be responding to voices. But James' symptoms were rarely crystal clear and, bafflingly, were embedded within and probably contaminated by his dilapidated mental state. He was disoriented and while it was difficult to say how forgetful he was because he said so little, and invariably gave little indication that he was listening to what was being said to him, the belief was that his memory was very poor.

A brain scan had been requested but James had become too distressed to undergo the procedure. The opinion was that if left to his own devices he would not survive, for he was oblivious to nearly all that was going on around him and unaware of what he needed to do. His coordination was also poor and he would occasionally fall as he slowly made his way around the ward. His daily life was governed by prompts and assistance to do the most basic of things, all passively and unquestionably accepted. The consensus was that James would never leave hospital to go home. But what would a return home mean to him anyway?

James had been living alone before his admission, in circumstances as dilapidated as his mental state. Receiving state benefits, he was barely surviving. This was not the consequence of living on a limited income but was more to do with his inability to manage his life. He would lose his money, spend it unwisely, be taken advantage of by those who viewed his flat as a place to shelter, and he would either forget to buy food or maybe he just didn't see it as a priority. He was as thin as a rake and he was only remotely acquainted with cleanliness and personal hygiene. He had come to the attention of the psychiatric and social services having been arrested on several occasions for shoplifting and disturbing the peace. He had been banned from bars and pubs for fighting, threatening behaviour, shouting profanities and swearing. On occasions police had arrested him for being drunk and disorderly but he could never pay any fine as he was unemployed and was unquestionably unemployable.

One evening, James having been involved in yet another fracas, the police had invoked the Mental Health Act and taken him to a 'place of safety'. This had been a police cell, but within hours he was admitted to a psychiatric hospital as an involuntary patient. And in this 'place of safety' he noticeably declined.

I saw James on several occasions. I was as perplexed as everyone else. Was James dementing? Even though his withdrawn and distracted state made assessment all but impossible this was not in doubt. Yet the picture was not typical of any of the common dementias. And then there were James's psychiatric symptoms. Often ambiguous, sometimes dominating his daily life, at other times not.

It was a Monday and another fruitless meeting with James was coming to an end. This had been quite a lengthy session as today he was withdrawn. On other days his agitated state meant our time together could be measured in seconds, but today, sitting opposite me, he allowed me to talk to him, even though there was no suggestion we were having a conversation, for as was often the case, he was lost in his own world of thought. A world that no one had come close to understanding. I had tried to test his memory and recognition but if there had been flickers of engagement any words he spoke were random and unclear. Occasionally his eyes would scan the room but they never detected anything of interest and having looked around he would once more stare not so much at you, as through you.

Enough time had passed. There was nothing more to be gained and, although I suspected that such was his indifference James could have continued to sit there for an age, I stood up. "Why don't we go back to the ward, James? I'll walk with you." Unexpectedly he looked up at me and in that moment his face was bathed in the sunshine that was coming through the window behind me, and in that moment I glimpsed it. A golden-brown ring on the edge of his iris.

Wilson's disease is a rare genetic condition that leads to a build up of copper in the body, mainly in the liver and brain. If left undiagnosed and untreated, it can result in irreversible dementia and is eventually fatal. And a characteristic sign of Wilson's disease, although not always present, is a brownish pigmentation of the cornea, known as Kayser-Fleischer rings, which are caused when deposits of copper build up at the front of the eye.

Aside from dementia, the symptoms of Wilson's

disease include tremor, poor coordination, slow movements, an unsteady walk, speech abnormalities progressing to a complete inability to speak, personality changes, depression, anxiety and psychosis. We had a probable diagnosis.

James's case notes named Angie, his sister, as his next of kin. She had never visited James but a social worker I spoke to had met her and said she would probably welcome a visit – even though she had cut herself off from James years ago, in large part because of her brother's conduct, she might want to know what had caused her brother 'to fall apart'.

However, my wish to see James's sister was not simply to share a diagnosis. Wilson's disease is an inherited dementia. It is an autosomal recessive disorder, which means in order to develop it you need to inherit two abnormal genes, one from your mother and one from your father. If both parents have the abnormal gene then a child has a one in four chance they will have Wilson's disease. While there is an equal probability they will be completely unaffected, there is also a two in four chance they will not have the disease itself but they will be a carrier, because in this instance they have inherited one abnormal gene. And carriers can pass the abnormal gene on to their own children.

Angie was a bright and cheery mother of three. She welcomed me in and immediately we connected. She was one of those people who you know within minutes you are going to like. I thanked her for seeing me so quickly. She thanked me for taking the time to visit and she said it was no problem at all as she was home most days.

Married, with three children under the age of eight, she said she couldn't imagine how anyone could find time to have a job as well. And as for a social life, that was a distant memory! As she talked about her husband and her children, what impressed me was not just how pleasant she was, but the sheer everyday normality of her life. Dementia does not respect good people, those who work hard, harbour ambitions for their children, families who simply don't deserve tragedy. Instead it cuts a swathe across society destroying the lives and relationships of decent people.

I told Angie that James had Wilson's disease, an incurable dementia. I think too much time had passed, and too much unpleasantness had happened for her to be upset or shocked, but she was undeniably saddened. She told me James had been a bricklayer and had always been a bit of a 'Jack the Lad' but without a bad bone in his body. He liked a drink, had plenty of friends, loved his sport, and was never without a girlfriend, most of whom were quite stunning. In essence James enjoyed life. Not so much at the time, but with the benefit of hindsight, Angie said there were a few early signs that James was changing, in particular the way he started to treat his girlfriends. Commitment was a word rarely to be found in James' vocabulary anyway when it came to women but his manner changed. It wasn't that he was simply more promiscuous – he became callous as well.

What's more, he became unreliable, and eventually unpredictable. He began turning up late for work, letting people down, unexpectedly turning up and then: "There were so many times he'd say he'd pop over to see us, sometimes he did, sometimes he didn't. Not a word, just nothing. Sometimes he'd arrive really late. I mean really late and he didn't seem to care. It drove my husband mad. Not a word of apology, just, I don't know, just selfish."

"But weren't there any physical signs that might have made you think James was unwell?" I asked. "Not really. Well, possibly but we just thought he was drinking too much. Sometimes you couldn't make sense of what he was saying because he'd speak really softly and his words were slurred. And he could be all fingers and thumbs, dropping things, knocking stuff over. Oh yes, and his hands sometimes shook. That was strange. But again we thought it was the drink. Thinking about it, he didn't look well but he just wasn't nice to have around so we were more angry with him than anything. Nothing major happened, it was like months passed and he got worse and we just didn't want anything to do with him. He wasn't bothered and he sort of drifted out of our lives. I used to hear the odd stories. How he'd got into bad company. The fights, the police, how he was in psychiatric hospital... Honestly, I didn't want my children to be anywhere near him. Now... I feel guilty. He was ill and I never realised."

There was little more that could be said. A poignant moment had been reached, one that was clearly upsetting for Angie, for she now felt that she had failed James. But this was not the end of our conversation – in some ways it was the start. The beginning of knowing what had happened to her family, and what she now needed to find out.

When I told Angie about James's condition I hadn't mentioned that Wilson's disease was an inherited dementia for that was not something you blithely tell someone without thinking what needs to be said and how best to say it. Yet, if truth be known, I was thankful to be sitting with Angie for if there was one good thing that could come out of the awfulness of James's plight it was the opportunity to help his sister, for it was vital she be checked for the condition, especially as an early diagnosis of Wilson's disease ushers in the prognosis of a relatively normal and healthy life. Nothing Angie had said and nothing I had observed had given me reason to be concerned. But there was always the possibility that Angie was a carrier and there were her three young children to consider. This was a conversation that now had to be about her, no longer one that was about a brother from whom she had distanced herself for the sake of her children. The irony was that here was I about to introduce their uncle back into their young lives. As I was reflecting on what I would tell Angie, she unwittingly opened the door herself and our conversation went down a path I never anticipated.

We were talking about how she had no cause to feel guilty when Angie suddenly said, "It was different with Andrew." Angie's words, softly spoken, were a bolt out of the blue. My first question was not how was it different with Andrew, but more pertinently who is Andrew?

Andrew was Angie and James's eldest brother. He had been a long-stay patient in a large psychiatric hospital in Scotland, but now at just 45 years old he was living in a nursing home in a state of advanced dementia. He had left home when he was 16, joined the merchant navy and was rarely part of his family's life thereafter. "Andrew and Dad never got on. And with their quick tempers we were all relieved when Andrew said he was leaving home. But Dad missed him terribly. You see the problem was they were too much alike. Anyway, mum died [from breast cancer] and Dad was never the same after that. He sort of gave up and rarely spoke about Andrew. I think he felt let down that he hadn't come home for mum's funeral. Then ages later we got news that he was living in Liverpool, then Glasgow, but we rarely heard much from him. Then we were contacted by this woman he'd been living with, who told us he had gone weird and Andrew was in a mental hospital. Me and Dad went to see him but he didn't know us and we couldn't get through to him. The doctor said he was like this most of the time and it was because he had pre-senile dementia."

"When was this?"

"Nearly five years ago. I knew nothing could be done. I knew he wouldn't get better, so I made my choice to move on. Not forget Andrew, more to let him live in my past. A brother I never really knew. Not like James."

I explained to Angie the nature of Wilson's disease in a way that I hoped would help her understand what the illness was and what it meant to her family. I wanted her to integrate this knowledge into the story of her life and, through understanding, gain some control over her response to the disease. She took the news well, better than I could have expected. We talked some more but I knew she needed some time on her own, if for no other reason than she had to prepare herself for her husband coming home from work to be told news that she knew would worry him, because he was a man who never coped well with uncertainty and not knowing. I told

Angie we would need to arrange for her to have some tests to determine whether she was affected in some way by Wilson's disease, but in the meantime I would pay a visit to Andrew. She asked whether Andrew's dementia might be a coincidence but given we were faced with an inherited pathology I said that, while this was possible, it was not likely. A week later I travelled to Scotland.

I found Andrew sitting in the lounge of the care home staring into space. "Andrew?" Nothing. I tried again. "Andrew." No reaction at all. I was told that he was like this all the time. Unresponsive, oblivious to all around him and totally dependent on his carers. I asked the home manager whether she had been told Andrew's diagnosis but beyond saying "he has dementia" she did not. I asked whether I could look at the notes that had accompanied Andrew to the home, but there was nothing more than a report from the social worker describing his needs and a discharge letter from a consultant psychiatrist reiterating this was a patient with advanced dementia of "unknown origin".

So this is why I came to be in the medical records office of a large psychiatric hospital looking through Andrew's inpatient notes. Most of the hospital had closed but within the still splendid grounds there remained an acute facility that was a hive of activity in an otherwise moribund setting. However, I was well away from the vibrancy and often frenetic atmosphere of what constitutes an acute psychiatric unit. Instead I was on the first floor of the main building, for years closed to patient care but still home to various administrative and support services. The shabbiness of the place bore witness to the hospital's decline, yet despite years of neglect it remained an imposing building. High ceilings, wide corridors, impressive framed paintings of hospital superintendents from bygone years were testimonials to the investment and pride that once characterised this and similar sanctuaries built to care for society's most vulnerable. Yet now they were little more than anachronistic buildings. An unwanted legacy, a source of unwelcome memories that these hospitals too often ceased to be havens of compassion and instead became places of suffering for those who were abused, tormented and abandoned by society on the so-called 'back wards'.

The bundle of notes was thick. A ragged brown file contained pages and pages of ward entries, records of sessions with psychiatrists and the occasional social worker, often unintelligible, and a few letters to Andrew's GP describing his decline into a pre-senile dementia. All little more than testimony to bureaucracy, institutionalisation and therapeutic inaction. My mood sank as I appreciated how thousands of words could say so little. There was little understanding of Andrew's illness and even less regard for the person who was dementing before their eyes. Yet in the midst of this totality of inconsequential information there was an unexpected flash of insight. I found an entry, probably written by a junior psychiatrist given it was simply a few words following a routine ward round (but with nothing other than an indecipherable signature it was impossible to tell). It read, *"No change. Not poss. to assess..... [unintelligible]. Head wound minor healing. .... [unintelligible]. Fell on ward again today. Conversation not poss. Slurred. ?Wilson's D. Rview [sic]"*

And that was it. There was no review. Or at least no report there had been one. No investigations documented. Wilson's disease was not mentioned again. This was the closest his doctors ever came to making a diagnosis, but with the knowledge I now had I was certain that two brothers separated by years of disaffection were now united by a shared fate. Wilson's disease had destroyed both their lives. However, for Angie, hers was to be a happy ending. Tests and genetic screening showed she had not inherited the abnormal gene. To her immense relief not only was she free from the disease but so were her children. This was to remain the tale of two brothers.

SIX

Him and his weird ways

Grace's father was holding centre stage. "I want to speak to him. He's a dirty old pervert and he needs to know he is. And how we feel… do you know how we feel? How upset our daughter is?" To put it mildly, he was fuming. Her mother, reserved and shy, looked down awkwardly but you could tell she too was angry. Or maybe more perturbed? It was difficult to know for she was saying very little. We tried to explain, console, calm but to little affect. However, I was adamant there was going to be no confrontation with Mr R. Had he done wrong? I wasn't sure. He was certainly not depraved. You could say he'd acted unwisely but his heart had been in the right place, although in all probability that wasn't correct either for his heart had been lost. Lost to Grace, a 16-year-old girl on work experience as part of her Year 11 life skills studies.

"Don't give me any of this dementia stuff. He knew what he was doing. He scared Grace half to death. She's stopped going out. She goes to school and comes home, and that's it. At weekends she stays in her room. That man has scarred her. Him and his weird ways." But I wasn't talking about Mr R's dementia. This was a more complex state of affairs.

Mr R had been admitted to the care home around a year ago. From the start everyone commented there was something strange about him. Some said he was just different, others said he was odd, even 'creepy', but most agreed on one thing: he was harmless. As months passed, the consensus was that Mr R could be peculiar, at times challenging, but in essence he was simply an eccentric, elderly gentleman. And his eccentricities were probably the reasons why he'd never married and had always lived alone.

As a result of a stroke 15 months earlier, Mr R now required a wheelchair. He'd been admitted to hospital having been found lying unconscious on the landing outside his housing association flat. It was an unappealing block of flats that people lived in through necessity not choice. This was true for Mr R but it didn't trouble him at all. He'd lived there for years. It was comfortable and familiar and, while he had no friends, he was the 'local character' everybody liked. He kept himself to himself. A private, solitary man who now found himself living in the social setting of a care home, but that is how it had to be. There was no way he could have been discharged home. He could no longer manage the stairs, and while there was a lift, it would have been impossible for his cluttered – yet in a strange way, organised – flat to be retrofitted to accommodate the support and adaptations his left-sided paralysis now required.

Mr R had been in poor health for a number of years. Weighing more than 20 stone with diabetes and high blood pressure it was little wonder he'd had a stroke. Aside from the major stroke damage, the CT scan of his brain had also shown several small infarcts (areas of dead tissue) which probably accounted for the problems he'd been having managing his medication in the months before his stroke. The beginnings of vascular dementia (the second most common type) had started to undermine his competence and independence.

In the care home Mr R embarked upon a mission to restore his life to the one he had lived for years. He never wanted to come out of his room to be with others in the lounge. In fact, he rarely wanted to leave his bed. Within weeks his GP said she was concerned about his weight, while his carers were worried about his hygiene, for he perspired profusely. It was decided that Mr R should go on a diet.

Mr R complained bitterly but the doctor argued that he lacked mental capacity and hence was incapable of knowing what was in his best interests when it came to his health. Unfortunately attempts to enforce the decision failed to take into account the subversive wonders of the internet. For as his diet descended into what Mr R saw as food fit for rabbits and portions sufficient only for "a babbie", he ordered takeaways online and then, to supplement his meals, used online shopping to stock his wardrobe and shelves with a range of foods, cakes and biscuits. And then Mr R's strangeness stepped in.

A typical morning for his carers consisted of the expected struggles of caring for a hemiplegic, obese man who, having been washed and groomed, then refused to get out of bed, protesting it was too difficult to manoeuvre him safely, and anyway there were more important things to do, namely to ensure that the packets, tins and tubs of food were arranged in the precise order reflecting both size and colour. Then throughout the day he would pull the alarm chord to attract staff to his need for biscuits, chocolate or whatever other snack he favoured. When asked where this would end he said, "I'll be fat but happy. I might even have another stroke." He had mental capacity. He was being unwise but as the law states (Mental Capacity Act, 2005) foolish behaviour cannot be taken as evidence of mental incompetence.

Mr R spent his days in bed engrossed in his photo albums, not so much looking at the pictures as ensuring they were straight and none had slipped off their hinges. But why would he spend time looking at them? They were so monotonous. There were endless indistinguishable photographs of lampposts and trees, as well as, and somewhat disconcertingly, photos of people. A sequence of the same person, tens of them, and then no more until later in the album or, in another volume, another series of photos but this time of a different person. The photographs revealed how fixated Mr R could become. And he was certainly consumed with internet shopping. If it wasn't his photo albums occupying his time it was his favourite 'click and deliver' store. A whole host of items would turn up at the home, most completely irrelevant to his life and the opportunities he now had, but all contributing to the well-ordered clutter in his room. To put a stop to it, a team meeting decided there should be another mental capacity assessment because not only was Mr R cluttering up his room – his latest fad was buying coloured plastic beakers – he was imprudently spending his money and more than likely exceeding his credit card limit. However, this further attempt to act in his 'best interests' similarly failed when his meticulous recording of expenditure against income, monthly savings and sketches of how he wanted his room to look was found in an exercise book, once more supporting Mr R's competence, if not his common sense.

As months passed everyone became used to how Mr R would respond to suggestions and how he wanted to live his daily life. It wasn't just his need for routine, it was how he would become absorbed in the detail of what he might do or what was required, and everything had to be in good order. If it was not, he would fret until all was how he wanted it to be. Then there were his grandiose ideas. He thought a chandelier in his room would look nice. As would the nurses and carers, if he bought them all new uniforms styled to look like air hostesses. Sometimes his grand designs and eye for detail would come together, such as when the occupational therapist and physiotherapist from the hospital, concerned by his sedentary lifestyle, tried to find a way to get him out of bed. They recommended a more comfortable and supportive armchair, suggested a cushion for his wheelchair and said they would arrange for a hoist to transfer him from his bed. Mr R rejected the hoist but appreciated there was a need to mechanically transfer him from bed to chair and immediately went online to check out pulleys and cables with the intention of designing his own technically elaborate hoist. Some thought it was a delaying tactic, but it wasn't. It was just the way he was.

Could Mr R's behaviour be explained by his vascular dementia, which in typical step-wise progression was slowly getting worse? There were now days when he was muddled, sometimes drowsy. And his memory for recent events and experiences was clearly not as good as before. Yet after a 'bad' day or two his intellectual and memory functioning was always restored, although rarely to the level it had been. But was the vascular damage responsible for his behaviour? The short answer had to be no. The dementia may have exaggerated some of his inappropriate behaviour because he was now less able to inhibit his urges, but the thread that ran through his actions and desires was who he was, not the dementia he was now living with. Yet why he behaved the way he did was still an unsolved mystery.

Nobody could remember the camera being delivered, but that was not surprising given Mr R ordered so much online. Looking at his neat records he had bought it not long after he had arrived at the care home. It remained in its packaging, unused in his bedside cupboard drawer, unused that is until Grace arrived for her work experience. Immediately Mr R was infatuated.

Grace came to work at the home for six weeks. Her job was to be a companion to the residents. In no way was she a carer. She would have conversations in the lounge, fetch items residents might want from their rooms and sit with those who were too frail to leave their rooms. Or in Mr R's case unwilling to do so.

Mr R was his normal likeable oddball self and this

chimed with Grace who was a touch unconventional herself. She was kind, bubbly and always willing to indulge him and his eccentricities. Mr R, in his unworldly way, was charming. They got on and he became her favourite resident. Yet she was taken aback when he asked whether he could take a photograph of her. Not alarmed, definitely not threatened, just surprised. Over the coming days he regularly asked if he could take a photograph. Nothing offensive or suggestive, all of Grace smiling.

Grace confided in one of the senior carers for she had started to feel awkward but she didn't want to offend Mr R because "he's really nice, I think he's a bit vulnerable". She was reassured that he gets "obsessed with things. But he's alright. Don't worry" But this time he wasn't obsessed with things, he was obsessed with Grace.

Saturday morning. Another delivery for Mr R. He removed the packaging and was delighted to see the gift wrapping he had requested. He placed the little box under his bedside lamp and there it lay untouched until Monday morning. Well that had been his hope, but it was now afternoon and he was becoming agitated. He had pulled the alarm chord on many occasions and the answer from increasingly harassed staff was always the same, Grace hadn't arrived yet. Once more he pulled the chord and this time Grace walked in. She had been to school to hand in an assignment. Sensing Mr R was upset, she apologised even though as she did so she was wondering why she needed to say sorry. However she didn't have time to dwell on this because Mr R disrupted her train of thought by handing her the little box. "I got this for you. Please open it." As she undid the small bow and tore at the wrapping she thought she heard him softly say, "I hope you will be mine." Had he spoken those words? Grace momentarily paused not knowing whether to look at Mr R or not, but then fatefully she opened the box and there, resting on a satin cushion, was an engagement ring. "I believe the question I now ask is, will you marry me?" Stunned, speechless, Grace didn't know what to say or do. "Let me put it on your finger." Bemused, driven by impulse rather than forethought she turned and fled from the room.

One of the nurses saw Grace crying in the corridor and suggested they go to see the home manager. Having explained what had happened, all Grace was able to say was "I'm sorry" over and over again. She was convinced she had done something wrong. Maybe she had given Mr R the wrong impression. He was such a kindly man. It must be her fault, but how could he have thought they could ever get married? The manager explained to Grace that Mr R had dementia and this was muddling his thinking. Rather than absolving her of any responsibility, Grace took this as further reason why she was to blame. She hadn't understood his difficulties and, while she was just being kind and obliging, clearly she had misled him and that's why he'd misinterpreted her feelings. "I shouldn't have let him take all those photographs." "Photographs! What photographs, Grace?" The senior carer she had confided in had told no one.

Had Mr R been grooming Grace? What were his intentions? If she hadn't left the room what might have happened? What initially might have been seen as another example of Mr R's eccentric but harmless behaviour now acquired a sinister overtone. Which is how I came to be in a meeting with Grace's parents and some concerned professionals, colleagues from health, social services and education, who were probably more interested in the welfare of Grace than they were with the wellbeing of Mr R. In the previous hour I had met with Mr R for the first time. He was troubled that he was no longer able to see Grace. I told him, as had others, that she no longer worked at the home. This upset him for he was certain she was the kind of young woman he would like to marry. I was in no doubt he was an innocent abroad. There had been no grooming and the likelihood would have been that if Grace had accepted the ring and his offer of marriage nothing would have changed other than he would have introduced her to others as his fiancée. He hadn't even contemplated what would have happened at the end of Grace's spell at the care home. His infatuation was another example of the excessive zeal he brought to whatever, or whoever was his current preoc-cupation. Yet why did he behave like this?

Over the next few days I learnt a fair amount about Mr R. I even visited the garden centre where he'd worked for decades until he retired, and where he did odd jobs right up until his stroke.

Mr R had never left home, living with his widowed mother until she died aged 79. He then moved into the flat he was to live in for the next 15 years until his stroke. He described his father as a disciplinarian – remote and unaffectionate, the exact opposite of his anxious and fussy mother, who smothered her only child with affection. He described himself as bright. At school he enjoyed science and mathematics but he didn't do well. "I'd get stuck and do things over and over again, but it never came right so I'd never finish." From an early age he'd started collecting all sorts of things. He would arrange and rearrange his collections of conkers, cigarette packets, rubbers, butterflies, milk bottle tops, even misshapen pieces of coal until "It felt right. And then I'd count everything I had. That felt good". Even though he knew his behaviour infuriated his father, who couldn't cope with his son's habits and tantrums when his routines were upset, he couldn't help himself. Mr R could only recall one holiday with his parents, a long weekend in Dymchurch. He thought he was possibly 12 years old. On the way, travelling by coach, he counted all the lampposts they passed. Out loud. "Dad was furious, but I couldn't see why. I had to do it. Anyway, mum didn't mind. She was nice like that."

Mr R left school with no qualifications and no ambitions. He just wanted everything to stay as it was, but that was never going to be possible. He liked nature and his mother spoke to a neighbour who worked at a garden nursery. She wondered if there might be a job for her son. There wasn't but it was to be the path he would one day tread. He got a labouring job on a nearby farm. He liked being outside, working on his own, knowing what he needed to do, with no interference from anyone. From the farm he got a job as a gardener at a large country house. But when he was told to buck up his ideas because everything he did took an age he got so upset his mother again asked whether there was job at the nearby garden nursery. This time there was. And here Mr R spent the rest of his working life, seeing it grow from a cluster of greenhouses into a modern-day garden centre. But for Mr R nothing really changed. Behind the scenes, far away from customers he carried on as he always had. He grew seedlings, he pruned the trees and shrubs, he moved trays of plants, he tidied up and not once did he want his life to be different. I talked to one of his work colleagues who had known Mr R for years. He confirmed all Mr R had told me. He was a solitary man who was uneasy in company, liked his routines, was meticulous in all he did, and yes, at times his ways were odd, but he was harmless. A man who wanted little from life. A man with undiagnosed Asperger's Syndrome.

PART III

Dementia together

"Being is more important than doing, the heart is more important than the mind, and caring together is better than caring alone"
– Henri Nouwen

SEVEN

Until death do us part

Mr and Mrs Evans were a devoted couple, who to all intents and purposes had lived an idyllic life. He had been a teacher, she a nurse. Married for nearly 60 years, they had three children, eight grandchildren and their lives were now enriched by the joy of great-grand-children. Not only were there family holidays but two of their granddaughters would frequently stay over, so fond were they of Gran and Poppa. They even lived in a whitewashed cottage and while it was not thatched there were roses around the front door.

They had met in 1944 when Geoffrey Evans was repatriated to a field hospital near Portsmouth having been wounded a few days after D-Day. His tank had been hit by a shell and he was in a sorry state. His wounds were serious but his mental state was of greater concern for he was the only survivor. Not only comrades but dear friends had been lost. Nurse Eleanor Squires tended his wounds for the 17 weeks he was in the hospital. As his body recovered she would make time and seek reasons to be with him. She knew what was happening. It's what they as young nurses had been warned against. She had fallen for a wounded serviceman. On reflection it was his fragile state of mind that nourished their relationship for he needed to confide and share his guilt. He believed he was not a better man, so why had he survived? It was little surprise she was attracted to this caring, sensitive, softly-spoken man. After he was discharged to a convalescence hospital, followed by extended home leave, they kept in touch by letter, corresponding more and more frequently.

By the time Geoffrey was again fit for action the war was drawing to a close and he never returned to hostilities. Eleanor had continued to nurse and, looking back, it is remarkable how their romance blossomed given they saw so very little of each other. After Portsmouth she was transferred first to London, and then to a hospital near Preston – nowhere near to Cardiff, where Geoffrey was recuperating at home with his parents.

With the war over and optimism in the air they were engaged within months and in 1947 they married. There followed decades of happy marriage. A close couple, they moved around the Midlands as Geoffrey pursued his teaching career, eventually becoming headmaster of a boys' grammar school. Knowing she wanted children more than a career, Eleanor was happy to nurse whenever she felt the need and time allowed, and there were always nursing jobs to be had. However, in her early 50s with her husband settled and her children no longer needing her as they once did Eleanor surprised herself and nursing again became her career. Over a period of ten years she went from staff-nurse to sister in charge of a demanding orthopaedic ward before ending her working life as a nurse manager.

Retiring at the same time, the Evans enjoyed short breaks and long holidays in Normandy, an affinity borne out of the circumstances under which they met. Geoffrey was fluent in French and such was their enjoyment of France they regularly rented a holiday home near Deauville for the entire summer and this became the setting for family holidays that embraced all the generations. However, with age Geoffrey had to face up to the limitations diabetes and high blood pressure placed upon him. Eventually he came round to the idea, probably at the behest of his children, that maybe the time was right to be less adventurous. However, this was no surrender to the ravages of passing time. Instead Geoffrey turned his hand to creating a spectacular cottage garden. There was a man in the village who had tended their garden while they holidayed abroad and he was a fine mentor.

Geoffrey had always had a flair for acquiring passions and once in the grip of one he would throw himself body and soul into his new venture. Like a sponge he would soak up all he needed to know. Gardening was no different. Soon his garden was glorious to behold; a blaze of colour, abundant with summer fruits and berries. And this was their comfortable and cosy life as Geoffrey and Eleanor moved through their late 70s into their mid-80s. Geoffrey, despite his years, always looking forward, planning and hoping while, if truth be told Eleanor was heading in a different direction, becoming more and more melancholic.

It was his wife's mood in the spring of 2005 that began to trouble Geoffrey. She had been subdued for much of the winter but this had been her way these past couple of years. Dark days and bleak winter weather exacted an emotional toll but the hope was that come the spring she would be her old self. But not this year. Not only did her mood not lift, she began to withdraw, spending hours saying little, often appearing distracted. As autumn set in something needed to be done. Eleanor was now spending hours in bed and even having got up she seemed weighed down, sometimes perplexed by what she needed to do.

Geoffrey did all he could to lift his wife's spirits. He would encourage her to sit with him in the conservatory so they could gaze into their garden bursting with its last beauty and enjoy the autumn sunshine. Vivid shades and tints of scarlet, gold and russet vying for attention, berries glistening with morning dew, trees and hedges shedding their autumnal foliage. As the crisp and withered leaves tumbled and fluttered on the autumn breeze, Geoffrey could be momentarily content and he would turn to Eleanor and say, "It's as if we are watching the leaves dance." Yet it was if Eleanor was seeing nothing at all. Expressionless, passive, emotionally unmoved Geoffrey was once more faced with a reality he was struggling to cope with.

Geoffrey persuaded Eleanor to go to the doctor for a check-up. The GP diagnosed depression and an anti-depressant was prescribed. Eleanor's mood lifted, her motivation improved and she was more aware, but as the months passed Geoffrey described his wife's plight as "going up a down-moving escalator". There was some improvement, although Geoffrey sometimes questioned how much, but it was all such a struggle. Tragically this was because Eleanor's mood was a depression overlay. Unbeknown to anyone she was living with the beginnings of dementia.

A few months later I met Eleanor for the first time. It was difficult to assess her because she would avoid questions and was most comfortable when left alone. But as I gained her confidence and she started to relax she would talk, hesitatingly but more openly than she had for months. When gaps in her memory appeared she would confabulate and tell her stories. Not outrageous fictions, just accounts of how life used to be, but to Eleanor how life still was. I couldn't help but notice her intermittent slips of the tongue and how time and again she struggled to recall why I was sitting with her. Then there were her husband's reports of failings and errors, including problems remembering the names of her grandchildren and how on many occasions she did not know her great-grandchildren, children who not so long ago she had fussed-over and adored. She might walk to the local shops, no more than a hundred metres away and be gone ages. In the beginning Geoffrey had taken this as a positive sign for he believed she was enjoying being out, maybe chatting to neighbours in the post office. But one day, having looked out of the upstairs bedroom window, he realised it was because Eleanor was bewildered and uncertain where to go even though in all these years they had lived at No 2 The Green she would have walked to the village shops thousands of times. All in all, a diagnosis of probable Alzheimer's disease was not difficult to make.

Geoffrey was shaken but not devastated, for that was not his way. Instead he threw himself into learning all he could about dementia and as the months passed he began supporting and, as the dementia took hold, caring for his wife. My assessment of Geoffrey and his ways – and in no way is this meant as a heartless appraisal of his actions, for Geoffrey is one of the most honourable and compassionate men I have had the privilege to meet – was that he now had a new project to consume him.

For a man of 86, I don't know where he got his energy from. Geoffrey did not want practical support as he felt life had turned full circle. This is how his life with Eleanor had started. He had once needed her and she had not failed him; now their roles were reversed and he would not be found wanting. The problem was Eleanor was not always willing to accept her husband's tender ways. As Eleanor became more dependent, the less she accepted Geoffrey's caring efforts. At times it was because Geoffrey could be over-powering, fuelled by both compassion and unbridled enthusiasm to be his wife's carer. However, on most occasions it was because she had little very awareness of her vulnerability. If there was a flickering appreciation of her personal care needs, Eleanor's conviction was that she could do it all. At times chaos ruled her mind and her zeal to be the imposing woman who walked the wards with an air of authority would be fleetingly resurrected and she would pace the house preoccupied and muttering. If Geoffrey tried to talk to her she would stare through him and walk on by.

What had happened to their loving relationship? This question haunted Geoffrey. Eleanor was not only frequently distracted and nearly always resistive to his efforts to care; she was also quick to spit out spiteful comments that cut Geoffrey to the quick. Yet Geoffrey coped better with the heartless remarks than he did with the hours of silence. He had never realised how oppressive silence could be. For Geoffrey it was deafening because of what it told him about their marriage. While the children told him it was "the dementia, not Mum" he irrationally started to question the entire basis of their marriage. Had Eleanor always resented him? Had she wanted a career as much as he did and he had blighted her ambitions? Had she only pitied him in the beginning? Could it be that it was not love that had cemented their relationship, but pity, then children and then ... complacency or maybe just habit. He gained some solace in the garden, but his days were lonely and the nights worse, for he now understood the difference between being lonely and feeling alone, the latter resonating with desperate yearning.

As Eleanor glared, fought and screamed, caring became more and more challenging to the point where Geoffrey reluctantly conceded he needed help. Homecare workers started to visit. His children tried to keep his spirits up. "Dad you haven't failed Mum, nobody could have done more than you." While their words were comforting, they were the words of his children. He knew best, always had. He had failed, but still he tried. I would sit with him and while his questions were directed at me I could tell he was subjecting himself to the most critical self-examination.

"How do I get Eleanor to drink? I have a terrible time getting fluid in. She refuses nearly all the time, even a teaspoon of water. It's like she wants to die."

"She won't eat. Refuses everything, and if she doesn't, well this morning she spat out it out. What can I do?"

One time he asked, "How can I get my Eleanor to let me wash her?" And before I could say anything his voice broke as he said, "When you're close to someone, it's painful to know you're..., well, know your best is not enough."

Geoffrey was determined not to give up but emotionally bruised and physically worn out, a day arrived that he had never anticipated. Eleanor went to live in a care home. Geoffrey saw it as little more than a betrayal, confirmed in his eyes by Eleanor's behaviour, or more accurately her absence of behaviour. While staff at the home sometimes got a response from her, Geoffrey never did. Their relationship was now lost in the fog of Eleanor's dementia. He visited everyday and there was nothing. He was always there at teatime to help her drink her cup of tea, or eat a biscuit, but to no avail. He would arrange and then rearrange her room. He would bring more and more of her things in to prompt her to talk. He would show her photographs of their children, their shared moments, but there was not a hint of recognition, no flicker of emotion. He might as well not have bothered for Eleanor had somehow developed the capacity to stare through Geoffrey while glaring at him with nothing other than contempt.

And then I received a letter from Geoffrey. A heart-wrenching testimony to how he was buckling under the weight of his wife's dementia.

"I am finding it very hard to get over what I can only say feels like the loss of my wife... She is introverted and almost always refuses to talk. I am left blaming myself for my feeble, largely unsuccessful attempts to care for her as her dementia has worsened... I love her very much and thought she loved me. Can you, are you able to give me any solace in this matter. If I can be assured that she loves me I

think that I could bear what is happening more easily."

Eleanor was drifting toward the end of her life. Not days away, not even weeks, but certainly months. Such vagueness did not help Geoffrey, but it is difficult to accurately predict when death is close because so many indicators are the typical characteristics of advanced dementia – rarely eating, drinking little, withdrawal, unresponsiveness, passivity – but without doubt time was not on our side. Geoffrey deserved to have his question answered. He was wrong to doubt himself, question his relationship with Eleanor. But he had, and that was a given. When they were together he felt only pain, and while I had no doubt as Geoffrey told their story that theirs had been a close relationship personified by a deep love for each other, neither I, nor anyone else, telling him he was wrong to feel this way was going to make him feel better. A different tack was now required.

I told Geoffrey it was no longer about supporting, caring, doing, it was about being there. Not even talking. Just being close, sitting there, sharing a view, holding hands. Nothing more. And why? Because we are social creatures who are sustained by affection and belonging. From the earliest times of life the physical presence of someone who cares is comforting. Babies gaze in wonderment at their mothers and within weeks their eyes are following the movements of people, especially those they recognise. Infants, as soon as they can crawl, will do all they can to stay close to those they know. This growth in sociability is at the core of who we are. In dementia, what is there first, either because it is innate or the result of early learning, stays the longest. "So no more doing, Geoffrey, just be there." And unfailingly from then on he was. Just there. No tasks to be completed; no questions; not even conversation. He was simply there.

Days passed and then, inexplicably but joyously while sitting together in the sensory garden, she turned her head, looked at Geoffrey and without a vestige of contempt, she smiled. And that's all he needed. She knew him. He was doing something right. It was to be days before she smiled again but she did. As days turned into weeks Geoffrey would sit next to Eleanor sometimes reading, sometimes thoughtfully reminiscing and he might look up or cast a glance and every now and then there would be another smile. These flickers of recognition and apparent warmth kept him going. On occasions Eleanor weakly, barely perceptibly stroked his hand. Sometimes she tugged the sleeve of his jumper. Theirs was now a relationship of a different order.

Geoffrey eventually concluded that Eleanor did not truly know him, neither by name or relationship, but that no longer mattered. He was at any one moment in time someone whose presence was comforting to her. While he may have worn a thin veneer of familiarity such belief was no longer required by Geoffrey to sustain his conviction that Eleanor still needed him. And this is how their story concluded. Geoffrey, loyal and tender, committed to never giving up on his wife. As their new relationship started, it was to end. Their lives were once more entwined, albeit it was now Eleanor's fragile mind that nourished their relationship. But could it be, notwithstanding the ravages of dementia, that Eleanor was still attracted to a man who remained the same caring and sensitive person she had fallen for all those years ago?

EIGHT

Parent to a child

The very first time I met Steve and his wife, her condemnation of her husband's behaviour, "he's just like a child", should have been my Sherlock Holmes moment. But it was not to be, for too much of the story was still to be told. All I knew was the sanitised version, for that is all the GP had been told. Dr Appleton had asked me to visit because Steve's wife was struggling with the demands of caring for her husband who had been diagnosed with dementia three years ago when he was just 59 years old. Steve was once more to her 'a child'. Judith, tired certainly but more exasperated, spoke of how incapable her husband had become; of his need for her in all he did or more accurately could no longer do. All recounted with a strange absence of feeling. A peculiar quality of indifference shrouded all she said. Judith was undoubtedly committed, but to whom, or might it be to what?

After this first visit I understood why Judith was weary, on occasions feeling totally worn out. But I did not understand why she had consulted her GP. While acknowledging how tiring caring could be, she said she was managing and it appeared that she was. At times it must have seemed like she was living the '36-hour day', but she hadn't asked for any practical help and nor did she want any. "I'm coping, thank you." She was managing, she wasn't distressed, no sense of loss was articulated, instead there was an emotional detachment from Steve. Maybe this was how she was able to cope. It was all very matter of fact. Tasks to be done. Things to do. Irritation when Steve was slow to respond or dug his heels in but she had brought up three children so she knew what to do.

I paid Steve and Judith one more visit and having heard much the same as before I let the GP know there was nothing more I could offer. I was therefore somewhat surprised that just a month later there was a message from the GP asking if I could visit once more as Judith had been on the phone in a terrible state. Less upset, more angry, and saying she was at the end of her tether and she couldn't go on much longer.

On my return Judith was again composed but I suspect she knew that having telephoned the GP she would have to be more forthcoming. We talked for a while about how her life had changed over the past three years. This clearly wasn't easy for her because she was reserved and she probably had never had reason to divulge personal problems or even confide in anyone before. Most definitely not to a stranger, even one draped in a cloak of professional respectability.

Steve's dementia had been a shock and had clearly damaged their relationship. Affection and intimacy were distant memories. As Steve became more dependent on her for his personal care and she needed to sleep rather than be disturbed by his nocturnal roaming she moved into the spare room. Even though she disliked this move from normality for many reasons, more than anything she hated it because it meant as soon as she awoke she knew her life after 30 years of marriage was no longer as she wanted it to be. No moments of self-deception, just the immediacy of knowing life was now different, another day to endure rather than share and enjoy. But in truth moving into separate bedrooms had had no effect on their relationship. Steve had retreated into himself in the months following his diagnosis, closeness had dissipated and they hadn't had sexual intercourse for "two years or more. I don't know whether it was the dementia or the drugs but he lost interest in sex early on. And I don't think it's ever bothered him".

Steve's dementia had also devastated his family. One daughter, the eldest, rarely visited as she could not bear to see her dad descend into the chaos of dementia. The loss of a man once so able, so caring, so witty to becoming one whose thoughts and memories were too jumbled for even the briefest sensible conversation was too much to bear. The tragedy for Judith was that this was the daughter she was closest to, the one she might have been able to confide in. But it was not to be. Her youngest had delayed going to university for a year as she felt her mum shouldn't have to take responsibility for her father alone but it hadn't worked out. She was young, too emotional and as Steve became increasingly stubborn she became angry with him, with the dementia and with her mum for not asking for help. She left for university resenting her father, in all likelihood feeling guilty and, probably in an effort to cope, she only returned home fleetingly. She too was living with her memories – but for Judith this was not an option.

Judith was resilient. Resourcefulness was without doubt engrained within her. Life was difficult but you get on with the hand you're dealt even though this one was especially tragic, devoid of any joy or pleasure. As Steve's dependency worsened Judith's life followed an unwavering script shaped by 'musts, shoulds and have tos'. The 'tyranny of the should' dominated their lives, and this was the source of much of Steve's aggression and Judith's exhaustion and exasperation.

We embarked upon some uneasy conversations, for Judith was quick to feel criticised. It was easy to see that she needed to feel in control and that set, invariably fixed routines helped her immensely – but the price she paid was conflict with Steve.

Getting Steve ready for bed was a particularly difficult time. Out of his day clothes, washed, teeth cleaned, using the toilet and into his pyjamas. Sometimes this might take nearly two hours. But it had to be done. There was normality to pursue, standards to keep up and the prospect of Steve wetting the bed was beyond the pale. But did it all *have* to be done when balanced against the time and effort needed to achieve it, as well as the distress it was causing Steve? And it clearly was causing him upset, for to see aggressive resistance as simply aggression denies the feelings Steve was experiencing. The feelings of being perplexed, degraded, ignored all contributed to his frustration. In the words of Martin

Luther King, "violence is the language of the unheard". Steve was aggressive but he wasn't a violent man; he was a man not being listened to and the salient question was whose interests were being served by the demands being placed on him?

Whenever a person is told they *must* do something we need to ask why, for to be told one *has* to do anything implies if you do not the consequences will be dire. If they are not, then why place anyone under the unnecessary stress of 'having' to do something? Might it not be better expressed as 'I'd rather' or 'I'd prefer'? All too often we fail to visit the other side of the coin to explore consequences as the 'tyranny of the should' becomes automatic thinking. It's just the way things are, but do they have to be?

I asked Judith what would happen at night if she didn't do all she was currently doing. For example, undressing Steve, whose response varied between trying to walk away or seemingly reaching out to undress Judith for he would pull at her clothes and twirl the buttons on her blouse; or holding on to him as she tried to wash his face or brush his teeth; or having taps running to encourage him to use the toilet; or even holding him down as he sat on the toilet. Is it any wonder that frustration and confrontation were in the air? Her first response was: "You mean never?"

"No, I was talking about flexibility. Being agile in how you approach the daily grind of caring. Does it matter if he goes to bed in his day clothes? What's the worst that could happen? He'd wake up in crumpled clothing."

And on most days Steve wasn't going anywhere. But might he be more inclined to change in the morning if he thought he was going somewhere, tapping into a routine of decades, namely getting ready for work? But if he still didn't want to get out of his now 'lived in' day clothes, in the spirit of hygiene rather than normality or perfection, then why not try to get him into his pyjamas every other night thereby halving the incidents of confrontation? Similarly with washing and cleaning teeth. While using the toilet was more problematic, we could look at his fluid intake during the evening, explore Steve's toilet habits to exploit historical routines and, if all else failed, keep the bedroom door ajar, the toilet door open with the light on and a night light gently illuminating the landing thereby helping Steve find his own way if he was to wake up. All suggestions to help not just Judith, but also Steve.

It took some time for Judith to change her ways for she needed to feel she was in control. But gradually she did and during one visit she told me "If only I'd known then what I know now we would have been spared so much heartache. Love is never supposed to hurt but..." and her voice tailed off, checked by emotion. Such feeling, surprising in a woman so understated, made me think she wasn't just talking about her relationship with Steve for I knew the way things were with her daughters weighed heavy. Equally I was sure that there was something else happening, a secret still to be expressed that would explain why there had been no discernible improvement in her mood. It wasn't that Judith was depressed or anxious, but anger and resentment always lurked beneath the surface, emotions that hadn't been affected by the fact that her relationship with Steve was now demonstrably less confrontational.

While forensic analysis and painstaking investigation can uncover a person's innermost thoughts and feelings, at other times it's just serendipity. This is how it was to be with Judith. She had cancelled an appointment and we rearranged for me to visit a few weeks later. On that day, just minutes before I arrived, Judith had cause to say to herself 'no more'. Within minutes of me arriving the outpouring began. Disgust and horror, embarrassment and shame fused into a single intolerable emotion.

Steve had exposed himself in the front room and as Judith walked in she was confronted by him masturbating. Judith could no longer cope. As the words came tumbling out she told me it had been going on for months, at first occasionally, but now it was nearly every day. Telling him it was unacceptable and offensive, reminding him over and over again that he was degrading himself, had no effect. So she found herself shouting at him, storming out of the room and, she admitted, slapping his face on more than one occasion.

Yet this made no sense. How could this intelligent woman reconcile two evidently incompatible observations? Judith had told me that Steve had lost his sex drive more than two years ago, but what more evidence did she need that she was wrong than her husband masturbating most days? But Judith did not believe she was holding irreconcilable views, for she saw his masturbation not as evidence of a sexual urge but as a symptom of his dementia. She had read that 'sexual disinhibition' could be a symptom and hence this was what she was grappling with. Not a man in his early 60s giving vent to feelings of sexual frustration.

Unfortunately Judith had fallen prey to what is referred to as 'diagnostic shadowing', which is a fate that even in these more enlightened times befalls far too many people with dementia. Namely, once a person is diagnosed with dementia everything that happens after the diagnosis is attributed to the diagnosis. It doesn't matter what they do: it's because they have dementia. They as a person are squeezed out of existence, their circumstances are ignored, and all that is considered is that their brain is not functioning as it once did. And this is what had happened to Judith. It wasn't a malicious act, just how people start to automatically think especially when a person's behaviour is out of character. The behaviour is taken as evidence that the person has disappeared leaving behind a husk that is simply playing host to symptoms of disease.

I knew explaining this to Judith was not going to be easy because it was clear to me that what I had now learnt went to the heart of their relationship and reflected how Judith now saw her husband. Her house was close to pristine, she was elegant and the photos around their home captured Steve as a similarly well-groomed man. They both had standards and if Steve was no longer able to maintain his then she would take responsibility for what he could no longer do. Consequently she had thrown herself into keeping Steve as immaculate as possible even when this meant hours of persuading, cajoling and too often facing up to Steve's abuse and aggression. And in the process Judith had fallen below a line, sometimes a fine one, that distinguishes a good carer from one who has lost their way.

Steve and Judith had been a happily married couple

enjoying an adult-to-adult relationship. Then tragically dementia stepped in and the presence of this third party changed everything. As time passed their relationship shifted in tone and became increasingly defined by Steve's progressive dependency. Steve was now a dependent adult, Judith a caring one. However, Judith couldn't sustain this relationship. As she pursued her need to 'keep up appearances' and as Steve became more dependent and vulnerable she began to see Steve more as a child. She knew best, she made the decisions and as her belief that her husband was more like a needy infant became an irrefutable conviction she ceased to be a caring adult and she became a parent to Steve.

An unintended consequence of this 'infantilisation' of Steve was the impact it had on their intimate private lives. Steve had never lost his sex drive. In the beginning stress, fear, distraction, depression may have conspired to diminish his desire, but as awareness dissipated and he gained respite from the indescribable emotional turmoil of the early months, his sexual need resurfaced, by which time Judith was in a very different place. She had a 'child' to look after and it was this 'child' who wanted intimacy and intercourse, but her inability to reciprocate wasn't because she was exhausted, nor was it because having spent an age assisting Steve with his efforts to wash, toilet and get ready for bed it was impossible for her then to contemplate sexual intercourse. While tiredness and the tasks she needed to do may have contributed to how she felt, her disinclination was more to do with a profound psycholog-ical shift that had occurred. A parent-child relationship now existed. She didn't simply care for her husband, she now mothered him and to Judith sexual relations would in her mind be tantamount to abuse. You see, it was not Steve who was content with the sexual abstinence that now bedevilled their marriage: it was Judith.

She railed against my interpretation, saying it was Steve, it was the dementia, not her. I reminded her how she had told me that when she was undressing Steve he would fiddle with her buttons as if trying to undress her. Might this suggest a sexual interest? No it didn't. She knew what she knew and that was not the explanation.

Having listened at length to her protests and failing to get Judith to see how Steve might be feeling I decided to seize the moment and provoke a response. Judith had been struggling for too long to be left in a state of debilitating denial. I said I'd have to leave soon and when I do, "Why don't you and *your husband* have some time together? Intimate time. Why not go upstairs and lie on the bed together. If you do I think you'll find Steve has got a sexual drive." Judith glared at me, then looked away and fell silent. And that silence said more than words could ever have done. This intelligent woman knew I was right, yet in her heart, as the passing of time was to reveal, she was never able to regain her sexual desire for Steve. And in no way was I surprised for their relationship had changed beyond all recognition, and a change as profound as Judith was experiencing cannot be set aside simply because one would like things to be as they once were. But at least she now understood… and sometimes that is all you can hope for. And with that understanding Judith, as resilient as ever, coped. In some small way Steve's voice was once again being heard.

NINE

Things are not always what they seem

Mrs C was the matriarch. Her personality and presence dominated her family. Even when her husband was alive her word was final and woe betide anyone who spoke unkindly of her. Her tongue was sharp, her outlook unforgiving and her manner stern. Suffice it to say she was not the easiest of women to know, and probably nearly impossible to live with. And her daughter-in-law who had been terrorised for years was no longer slow to voice her feelings to all who would listen. But why did she now feel able to speak out? It was because she no longer feared being ostracised by Mrs C, or more likely her husband being badgered into submission and apologising on his wife's behalf, and the reason for that was five years ago Mrs C had been diagnosed with vascular dementia. While "she's still impossible" she was no longer the fearsome woman of old. Yet this did not mean family life was harmonious or easy at all, for Mrs C's dementia had exposed a rift that had lingered beneath the surface of the relationship Helen, who was Mrs C's daughter-in-law, had with Claire, Mrs C's daughter.

Claire worshipped her mother and wouldn't have a word said against her. Yes, she wasn't the easiest person alive, but Claire said: "She's a character. She's strong-willed and she has spirit. Without Mum, Dad would never have kept this farm going because it's been tough, sometimes for years on end." That was true, for dairy farming could be demanding on the body as well as the mind, with early morning milking seven days a week and milk prices that fluctuated wildly. Either because of no time or no money, holidays and treats had always been few and far between for Claire and her brother, Tony.

Claire lived on an adjacent farm having married David, who a few years back had inherited his father's farm having worked on it all his life, except for three years when he went away to agricultural college. Helen lived on the family farm having married Tony, Mrs C's youngest child. But she hadn't just married Tony; she had married a way of life as well as marrying into a family where Mrs C dominated everyone and everything around her. Not long after they married, Helen had been on the receiving end of Ms C's wrath.

Helen resented the way Tony was downtrodden, most of the time treated as a hired hand whose opinions rarely mattered. She was protective of him but she also knew that voicing her anger would probably make matters worse, so she silently bridled at Tony's treatment. Yet when it became clear that Mrs C was equally dismissive of Helen, seeing her as just another pair of hands to help around the house and farm, enough was enough. She was not prepared to be treated in this way if for no other reason she was not only Tony's wife, she was also respected as the very busy manager of a nearby garden centre. She let Mrs C know how she felt and, while the ensuing argument was bad enough, what was worse was that Mrs C never forgave, nor did she forget. From there on in their relationship was at best polite, and at worse distant and acrimonious.

Helen had confided in Claire not because she wanted her support but more because she needed someone to simply listen and understand, and she was sure she would for she saw how Claire was treated in very much the same way as Tony. But no, Claire came to her mother's defence. There was no middle ground, no six of one, half a dozen of the other. Claire felt Helen was the one who didn't understand and in turn had been disrespectful and ungrateful, for wasn't she living in a lovely farmhouse provided by her parents? Helen realised that despite it being transparently obvious that Mrs C was not only difficult but at times her behaviour could be insufferable, in Claire's eyes her mother could do no wrong. Helen sought out David, for surely he saw how obnoxious Mrs C could be? It was a fruitless conversation: although he listened, a mix of reticence and loyalty to Claire meant he was never going to side with Helen.

So that was that. The tone was set, years passed and the family muddled along. Like actors in a play they had their roles. Tony meek and compliant, Helen inwardly seething, David silent and Claire worshipping the ground her mother walked on. Mr C was taciturn and a man who didn't care much for feelings and relationships. He had more important matters to concern himself with and these revolved around the farm. And over them all reigned Mrs C, calculating, intolerant and despotic, yet also surprisingly adoring of her five grandchildren, Helen and Tony's two sons and Claire and David's son and two daughters.

In 2001 Tony's father died and he took over the running of the farm. Nothing in reality changed other than a huge weight was lifted off Tony's shoulders. He confided to Helen that he no longer felt he had to prove himself and he was sure that one morning, although he didn't know when, he would wake up and that unbearable and at times incapacitating feeling of being worthless would have gone. He told her that he had once contemplated suicide but had told no one. It was a year before he had met Helen. He had gone with his shotgun to the far south field, walked up Brock Hill, lay looking at the clouds and wondered if death might be more forgiving and peaceful than his life. But having been up since 4.30am he fell asleep only to be woken by his mobile phone ringing. It was his father demanding to know where he was, they had 'a good milker' down in the boggy field and they needed to get the cow back on her feet. Helen's contempt for her husband's parents deepened.

Mrs C was resilient in the face of her husband's death for she was undeniably a strong and resourceful woman but there were times you could tell she missed her husband being around. Helen found it impossible to feel any compassion. She couldn't, even when Mrs C had a stroke. She recovered well, although she remained a bit unsteady and some visual field loss persisted, which meant she would walk into things on her left side as if they weren't there. But a walking stick and a less adventurous, more homebound life were the common sense solutions. For several months all seemed well until Mrs C started to have episodes of muddle and confusion. These could last for minutes or sometimes hours. The doctor said these were transient ischaemic attacks (TIAs) and were quite common in people who had a history of stroke. Her family was reassured but as the weeks passed Mrs C seemed not to be recovering so well from her 'attacks'. Her confusion persisted for longer and even when not acutely muddled she seemed to be forgetting everyday things, on occasions mixing up her words when talking and her personal hygiene was not what it used to be. Mrs C was referred to a consultant psychogeriatrician but before he could see her she collapsed and she was rushed into hospital.

It had been another stroke, a minor one, but the CT scan of her brain showed Mrs C had sustained several small infarcts throughout her cerebral cortex, with one deep within her cerebellum. The consultant was in no doubt, Mrs C had vascular dementia. While he could not predict the future for there was no way of knowing when Mrs C would have more stroke activity, where in the brain this activity might be located and how severe it might be, the prognosis was one of more uneven cognitive decline from which there could be some limited recovery but overall the trend would be progressive deterioration.

Over the coming months Mrs C's family struggled, for as she became more and more dependent, she became less and less aware of her frailties. Or maybe she was just stubborn. She wouldn't listen to advice, nor would she accept help without there being endless persuasion and cajoling. I suspect if this had been the extent of their difficulties Helen and Tony would have managed, helped by Claire and the assistance provided by professional home carers. Unfortunately Helen and Tony were attempting to care for a woman whose personality remained as abhorrent and unpleasant as ever. She was ungrateful, impatient and self-opinionated. "She did it to spite us. She knew she couldn't manage the stairs," Helen protested. "The bloody woman isn't that daft." Mrs C had insisted she was going upstairs to the toilet rather than use the one next to the kitchen. Having only got part way she refused to go any further and simply sat down holding onto the handrail. There she soiled herself and it took over an hour to get her into the bathroom with her cursing and shouting, "You're hurting me, you just want me dead!"

Two homecare workers refused to visit because of Mrs C's contempt for them and it was not long before the homecare agency let it be known that they would no longer accept Mrs C as a client. Day after exhausting day Mrs C's behaviour eventually got the better of Helen and Tony. While Tony was prepared to do all he could to help his mother there was only so much he could do. Farm life was as busy as ever and, even if it had not been, he could not contemplate caring intimately for his mother. While some sons have a remarkable bond with their mothers that enables them to do all that is needed as they "lead with their love" (Hoag, 2014), Tony's attitude was not surprising – many sons feel the same way. As for Helen, who had by now given up her position at the garden centre to work alongside Tony on the farm and in the flourishing farm shop they had recently opened, she was finding caring for her mother-in-law all too much not only because of the huge demands it was placing on them as a couple but because she had discovered that she also could not forgive or forget.

Claire sat down with Tony and made it clear that in her view their mother was nowhere near as difficult as was being said. She'd just spent a few days with her and David and, yes, she was needy but, "Tony, she has dementia. Our poor mum has dementia. She needs us. What would Dad say if he could hear all the things that are being said about her? He'd turn in his grave." Claire knew where the finger of blame should be pointed. "You know as well as I do Helen has never got on with Mum. Their relationship has been terrible for as long as I can remember. Any little thing Mum does or asks for is like a red rag to a bull as far as Helen's concerned." All Tony's self-doubts came flooding back as he wondered whether Claire was right. Were he and Helen being too hard hearted?

Tony tried talking to Helen but as he feared Helen saw it all very differently and the rows between them started. Helen was aghast that Tony had sided with his sister and couldn't accept she was to blame. "Will I never be rid of this woman?" she yelled one evening and stormed out of the room.

It was the arguments with Tony that led a distraught Helen to confide in her GP that she could not carry on any longer. He suggested Mrs C went for a short stay in a nearby nursing home and he made a referral to the community mental health team for it was clear Helen needed someone to talk to.

"You want to put our mother in a home?" Claire couldn't believe Tony had agreed with Helen's suggestion. "How could you? Just because your wife hasn't got a compassionate bone in her body you're prepared for our Mum to suffer even more." But Claire need not have worried for it was destined not to happen.

Mrs C was even more vitriolic than usual when Helen and Tony, or more accurately Helen, put the idea to her one morning. "Over my dead body," Mrs C screeched. "That can be arranged," Helen retorted, and she threw back her chair back with such force it smashed into the dresser and over went the vase of flowers.

There was no way Mrs C was going to agree but a line had been crossed. Something had to be done. The community psychiatric nurse who had started visiting brought the family together to see what could be done to make everyone's life better. Nobody can remember whose suggestion it was but the germ of an idea probably came when Helen turned on Claire and said, "Well, you look after her then. She's your mother." Out of acrimony came a possible solution.

While Claire voiced reservations that her mother wouldn't be happy leaving her home, one she had lived in for over 50 years, she conceded there probably was no alternative but to share responsibility for Mrs C's care. And that's how it came about that Mrs C began to live one month at a time at each of her children's homes. Mrs C wasn't happy about the arrangement but as she said to all who would listen, "At least Claire doesn't bully me", and once more Tony felt the inadequate son he thought he no longer was, a son who couldn't do right by his mother even when she needed him most.

The arrangement had been in place for close to six months and while Helen admitted that each month away from her mother-in-law was bliss, the breaks did little to soften the blow when she returned. She continued to express a litany of complaints about Mrs C's conduct. "I hate her some days," she would say. She would carp about how lazy, uncooperative and sharp tongued Mrs C was: "If she wants something it has to be done now. But if we're exhausted and want to go to bed and she doesn't there's not a jot of consideration. Sometimes we don't get to sleep before the early hours." The psychiatric nurse was so concerned about Helen's relationship with Mrs C she visited weekly to keep an eye on how things were going. Helen would reassure her that despite everything she was fine. "I grit my teeth and get on with it. What choice do I have if she won't agree to go into a home?"

In contrast Claire was uncomplaining. She looked tired and reluctantly she agreed her mother sometimes needed some coaxing and on occasions she could be awkward but: "She's nothing like my sister-in-law describes. In fact now the children have moved away and David's as busy as ever it's nice to have the company." Was Mrs C dramatically different with her daughter compared to when she was with Helen? Quite possibly, because it was undeniable that hostility and acrimony ran deep between Helen and her mother-in-law, but it could also be the case that because of their poor relationship Helen was intolerant of behaviour that Claire took in her stride? As I have written on many occasions, behaviours that challenge are embedded within relationships, those who act and those who experience. And those who experience, their responses are affected by a host of factors, one of which will be the history of the pre-morbid relationship. For this reason we can only rarely expect a loveless relationship to be transformed into a caring relationship just because one of the partners, or in this case a mother-in-law, has dementia.

The stark contrast in how the two women were experiencing their caring responsibilities was why I was accompanying the psychiatric nurse on her visit to see Mrs C. Jeanette had been visiting for a few months and she thought it would be a valuable lesson for me to see how the quality of a pre-existing relationship could influence a person's ability to cope with caring.

There was no answer when Jeanette knocked on the front door. This was not unusual as "she's often out in the yard", and so we let ourselves in – and there was Mrs C dozing in the chair. Yet as we approached something didn't feel right. There was a strong odour of urine, but that wasn't it. It was her body position. She wasn't leaning to one side, she was more slumped across the armchair, and as we got closer what we thought was Mrs C snoring was in fact her quietly groaning. Jeanette touched her shoulder but she did not respond. We bent down and tried to sit her up but as we did so she screamed out in pain. Then we saw. Her face was bruised, her right eye was swollen and closed, and sickeningly her right arm was hanging at a grotesque angle.

Looking up from where Mrs C was sitting you could see into the kitchen. Why would anyone be blithely doing the washing up knowing such suffering was just metres away? "What on earth's happened?" Jeanette demanded as she strode into the kitchen. "What do you mean? Nothing's happened," was the indifferent reply. Jeanette was stunned and momentarily lost for words. I'd been kneeling by Mrs C but as I stood this seemed to be the distraction that prompted Claire to proclaim as if jolted out of silent reflection, "Oh that. She fell." I walked into the kitchen past Jeanette, who had gathered her thoughts and was now on her mobile calling an ambulance. "Claire, why don't we have a chat?" And as if I was a neighbour who'd unexpectedly popped round she said simply, "Okay. We could have a coffee?" – and without a shred of emotion she walked with me into the dining room.

You see it was Helen who was experiencing and describing the situation as it truly was. Stressful, exhausting, frustrating and at times nearly impossible to deal with. Her poor relationship with Mrs C had generated a degree of intolerance but being unhindered by either love or loyalty she could release her anger by grumbling and protesting, and at times screaming out at the top of her voice "I'll swing for that bloody woman one day!". It enabled her to cope, but it should also have been the voice that was being listened to. In contrast, Claire was as cowed and intimidated as her brother and just as he had done she had bottled up her feelings for years, but unlike Tony she had confided in no one. As her mother became increasingly dependent and demanding, and Claire took on more and more responsibility, her pent-up resentment could never remain bottled forever. And one morning Mrs C pushed her daughter too far.

The abuse was probably nothing out of the ordinary but on this occasion it was just a word or phrase too far and with volcanic force Claire reacted. Having struggled for an age to accompany Mrs C from the toilet with her mother cursing and condemning Claire for being as bad as Helen, she snapped and shoved her mother down the steps that led back into the lounge.

Mrs C's dementia had exacted a tragic toll on her family, but in truth the origins of this tragedy were to be found in the complex and unhealthy dynamics of a family who had never been able to be open and honest with each other. And when Helen had given them an opportunity to break from their emotional shackles all those years ago, such was the damage done to their children by Mr and Mrs C's parenting they were unable to speak out. As such they each suffered years more of psychological hardship and neglect. In contrast Mrs C's suffering at the hands of her daughter was fleeting in comparison – but as appalling nevertheless.

PART IV

The search for meaning

"Discovery consists of seeing what everybody has seen and thinking what nobody has thought"
– ALBERT SZENT-GYORKI

TEN

Tall, dark and probably handsome

People were wary of Elsie. They wondered what was going to happen next. Walking down hallways, through lounges, with her arm raised in the air. Bolt upright. Never her left, always her right. And never when sitting, always when walking. That was strange: only when walking. No one could ever recall Elsie raising her arm at any other time. Sometimes it was raised from the moment she left her chair. At others she would be ambling around the building, shambolic yet absorbed in what can only have been disorderly fragments of thought, for she was severely demented. When something within her changed, her pace would quicken, she would look fretful and her right arm would shoot up in the air. Whatever was going on had to be from within because around her all appeared the same. And with her arm held high, seemingly deliberate and determined, she would hold it there for ages. An action that belied her 85 years.

At other times Elsie would simply walk the building and be indistinguishable from any other aged resident who was on the move. Yet staff and visitors were always on edge when near her because at any moment that arm might fly upwards and when it did it had to come down – and would that be with equal ferocity? An elderly woman, small in stature with chronic bronchitis and probable Alzheimer's disease striking fear into others; the irony was not lost on some of the staff.

But why was Elsie acting this way? It made no sense, but why should it; she had dementia. Yet something had to be done because not only was she was intimidating; there had been incidents. As her arm shot up she had hit other residents. Once, a frail lady had been knocked senseless. Deliberate? Let's say opinion was divided. Elsie had also injured herself. On one occasion she had caught her arm on a fire extinguisher, on another she had cracked her knuckles on a handrail. She had never hit anyone when lowering her arm, but that had done little to calm people's anxieties.

The GP, to her credit, had been reluctant to prescribe antipsychotic medication having become aware of the extent to which these drugs may be of little or no benefit when managing challenges such as agitation and aggression in dementia, and knowing as well their association with stroke and falls. Following the incident when Elsie had rendered the resident unconscious, the GP had felt compelled to act and had prescribed Risperidone but within less than 72 hours Elsie was stumbling and soporific and the medication was withdrawn.

There was nothing that staff knew of in Elsie's

background that could offer any insights into her behaviour. Her history appeared unremarkable, and why should we be surprised when we hear this? After all, dementia affects normal, everyday people not necessarily the bizarre, the remarkable or the eccentric, although of course these characteristics offer no immunity! She had been married but her husband had died years ago. She had two daughters, one of whom was a regular visitor to the care home. Very occasionally her youngest brother and a sister would visit as well. Staff described her as having her moments. While most of the time she was happy to go along with what was suggested, hygiene was not her strongest suit, so washing and especially bathing could be challenging times. But away from the tasks of care she was no trouble. And while conversation was sparse she clearly enjoyed the company of others. She would sit for hours dozing and looking around, and then for some unfathomable reason up she would get and the next thing people would see would be Elsie walking around with her arm held upright. They would retreat and avoid her, and residents would be ushered out of her vicinity. Isolated within her social world, she would walk and walk until the moment of her choosing when her arm would descend. Inexplicable.

Her daughter could offer no clues other than to say "Mum had lots of obsessional habits", because Elsie's world was one of self-doubt and insecurity. It always had been. The dark, noises, strangers, even the future all conspired to worry her. Life after her husband died had been particularly difficult and she had relied heavily on her daughters for reassurance. Alone at night she would check, check and check again that windows were shut and doors locked. She would even check wardrobes and kick the eiderdown to make sure no one was hiding under the bed. And as for opening the front door to people she didn't know or after dark, the bolt and chain meant this was an unlikely prospect. So sitting in the corner of the lounge in the care home, diminutive and delicate, is it likely that she would feel anything other than anxious?

Talking to her carers, a couple said that while they couldn't be certain, it was possible that if someone in the lounge had called out or fallen or if there had been an altercation, they remembered Elsie walking around soon afterwards with "that arm stuck in the air like one of them lightning rods!". But they had thought nothing of it because on most occasions "it just sort of happens when nothing's going on". However, could this arm-raising be when the 'theatre of the mind' had stepped in to provoke the same behaviour? Anxieties linked not to the present but to her past could have done it, a past that now intruded into the present day with a significance that belied its historical remoteness.

If her behaviour was anxiety driven, why was her arm in the air? Was she preparing to fight people off? Was she seeking reassurance or protection by drawing attention to herself as a child would in a classroom when wanting to be excused?

Elsie was born in London. One of nine children, the third youngest. Her father was a milkman. More accurately an occasional milkman, for he was bedevilled with 'bad nerves'. Unsurprisingly the family were poor, regularly moving from one rented and cramped abode to another as Elsie's mother gave birth to yet another child. Fighting for attention and space, affected by her father's temperament and absences when he had to be admitted to the nearby asylum and ridiculed at school for her shabby appearance and ill-fitting clothes, Elsie was an anxious and timid child. One day at school when she was about 10 years old she dissolved into tears when a group of girls taunted her by calling out that her father was mad. She was inconsolable. Only after she was taken home by a teacher to be comforted by her mother did she calm down.

The anxious child became a nervous and diffident teenager who, at the outbreak of the Second World War, was evacuated with her classmates to rural Warwickshire. Thirteen years old and 150 miles from London, she might as well have been on the other side of the world. She was out of London and out of danger, but nothing felt right. The couple who had taken her in were kindly but had never had children. They didn't know the ways of a lost and bewildered child and hence must have found Elsie just as perplexing as she found life on the farm. Rumours about London being bombed and Nazi agents releasing poisonous gas into shops and people's houses did nothing to calm Elsie's anxieties.

After a week or two Elsie started to complain of an earache. It caused her to cry out at night. She wouldn't eat. She didn't want to go to school. More than once she was sent 'home' and, while Mrs Gregson did her best to console her, it was pointless. The doctor was baffled. Elsie's ear didn't look inflamed. It wasn't particularly tender to the touch, yet whatever he suggested nothing helped. Elsie pleaded to go home; the local evacuation committee eventually relented and she was put on a train back to London. And almost immediately she was cured. At home with mum and dad and her youngest brother she was fine. Not 'bouncing around with joy fine' but clearly relieved to be home. But her joy was to be short-lived. Having been restored to health Elsie found herself back on a train returning to the safety of rural Warwickshire. Days after having been placed back in the care of the Gregsons, Elsie's earache returned. Once more the Gregsons' family doctor was exasperated. Only when she was sent to see a specialist at the local hospital was a diagnosis made: 'hysterical earache'. While safe in the eyes of others, in fact fretting and worrying about her parents' welfare and believing she didn't belong meant Elsie felt anything but secure. And with each passing day, as her separation anxieties grew, she maladapted, and probably without a vestige of conscious intent she converted her dread and distress into a physical ailment. An ailment that was no less agonising because its origins were psychological.

Elsie returned to London and, with a sense of security and stoicism borne out of proximity to her parents, she bravely faced the deprivation and trauma of war. She spent nights in bomb shelters, saw the landscape change as the Blitz ravaged where she lived and she learnt not to stare when faced with the haunted looks of neighbours who had received what all dreaded, the telegrams informing them that their partners or sons were missing or had been killed in action. She survived.

Aged 18 she was conscripted into the Royal Air Force

and found herself posted to an RAF base in deepest East Anglia. These were to become happy times. She enjoyed the camaraderie and flirtations. The American servicemen based nearby were charmed by her 'cockney accent'. However, whenever she got a weekend pass she would head to London. A train into Liverpool Street and a couple of buses across north London and she was again where she most needed to be, home. Her family remained her emotional anchor.

As the weekend came to an end, she would head back. But this was wartime. The trains were unreliable. Sometimes her train would be cancelled, at other times it would leave late or be delayed on the way. Elsie's Warrant Officer had instructed her and all the other recruits: "If you arrive late at the station and the transport has gone you don't stay at the station. You walk to the base. Do otherwise and you will find yourself on a charge." And her train was invariably late.

The walk was two miles along a country lane hemmed in by dense hedgerows, all around enveloped in a darkness that only the heart of the countryside can bring. As Elsie walked past fields, over a stream, through woodland to her this was the middle of nowhere. Again this was not where she belonged. Shapeless shadows that with every step took on sinister forms. Were those leaves rustling in the wind or were they footsteps? All served to provoke fear in Elsie's heart. The insecure and nervous teenager was now an equally fretful and fearful young woman especially when away from what she knew and needed - her home. Frightened of what might befall her, convinced that lurking behind every tree and bush were strangers with evil intent, vulnerable but not helpless, Elsie arrived at a solution.

Elsie had recently discovered the pleasures of smoking, a joy that would one day evolve into a 50-a-day habit she would never forsake. Walking alone, consumed by fear Elsie lit up a cigarette, inhaled and with the tip glowing red she thrust her arm into the air and there it remained until the glow dimmed, when she would start over again. Why? To give the impression that striding down the lane was a tall, powerful man, probably dark and handsome who would be more than a match for anyone skulking in the undergrowth. With her fragile self-confidence restored, she negotiated that walk time and time again with a trepidation that was now within tolerable limits. She had matured. Still afflicted by insecurities and fears, invariably irrational she had learnt that sometimes she could cope. There was no need for a hysterical earache to return her to where she felt safe. Instead a savvy, street-wise solution was her salvation.

Unfortunately Elsie's life after the war continued to be affected by panic and irrational anxieties. She would fret and worry and on several occasions her mental state became so bad she was admitted to a psychiatric hospital. Now, living with dementia, confronted with uncertainties and the strange ways of others, who knows what foreboding coloured Elsie's thoughts and perceptions? But there, deep in her emotional memory, was an action that many years ago had served her well. With her arm raised she was soothed, and with reassurance came peace of mind. It was not a violent gesture. Any harm was innocently and accidentally inflicted. This was the action of a troubled woman who did not warrant suspicious looks and certainly did not deserve people backing away from her since this simply added to the strangeness and ugliness of her situation, perpetuating the very action all others wanted to stop. Contrary to what people were doing, she needed to be treated with compassion and tenderness.

I said to her carers, "Approach her with a warm, inviting smile and gently talk to her, comfort her, reassure her and if I am right her arm will come down." And it did, for this was not a story about dementia. This was the tale of a woman who long ago exercised ingenuity to find a way to travel alone down a road that to her no longer felt lonely. With a fresh understanding of Elsie, never again was she abandoned to dwell on her fears as she walked the hallways. She was now accompanied by people who cared, and although they were rarely tall, dark and handsome this did not matter, for that was nothing more than inconsequential detail.

ELEVEN

We are not talking infidelity

Spencer had found a new lease of life. He had been living in the care home for nearly a year, during which time his presence could only be described as anonymous. He was the sort of resident you never really noticed but if you did, you'd say, "He's a nice man. Quiet." He conveyed a sense of mild-mannered bewilderment. His speech was hesitant and sparse so it was more his way than his words that made you think that politeness was a feature of not only who Spencer once was but who he remained.

However, while his demeanour was gentle it could never be said he was happy. And why should he have been, living in a place he didn't understand, alongside people he didn't know, separated from the woman he had been married to for 51 years? As you might expect, only when his Peggy visited would he come to life and you would say he was happy. But nowadays those visits were becoming more and more infrequent. Not because her love for her husband had diminished but, as she would say, "Spencer was my legs, I was his brain." Affected by rheumatoid arthritis, Peggy's mobility had progressively declined. Once she had been a nurse working on a busy children's ward but now standing, let alone walking, was painful and so visits to Beacon Croft happened at best a couple of times a week. Yet in no way could physical discomfort influence the love she felt for her Spencer, a love that still ran deep and true. He had been her only boyfriend. She had known from the very moment he had plucked up the courage to ask her out that he was the one and, while her parents were against them marrying at such a young age, they eventually gave in when all could see how smitten their daughter was with the young car mechanic. So, aged just 20 Peggy married Spencer Whitby, a young man only seven months her senior.

Theirs was to be a particularly close marriage, probably because Peggy had been unable to have children. For years they had tried without success. Initially they felt luck was not on their side but as Peggy began to worry they paid a visit to their family doctor who referred them on to the hospital, where it was found that Peggy's fallopian tubes were blocked. She could never be pregnant.

It wasn't that much of a shock to Peggy because for a while she had been thinking something was seriously wrong. She was upset, as was Spencer knowing they would never have children but as a couple they were close, all else in life was good and so it was no surprise to friends and family that their relationship prospered. As Peggy's sister wrote in her card to celebrate their 25th wedding anniversary: "Peggy and Spencer. Together as one."

Yet physically they were no longer together as one. They had been torn apart by dementia. Peggy had been a devoted carer but as Spencer became more intellectually disabled she struggled to cope. Spencer was dependent on her for all his personal care and always she had to be watchful. Always, for night and day meant little to Spencer. But rheumatoid arthritis was to be the undoing of her ability to do all that was needed. With a heavy heart she agreed with the social worker that it was time for Spencer to move into a care home. There were tears, but these were Peggy's, because Spencer had reached a point where he knew little, if anything, about what was happening in his life.

From the very beginning, Spencer sought sanctuary in a corner of the lounge where he could sit away from others. It was immediately to the left as you walked in so most people failed to see the comfy armchair you could sink into and all but disappear. Their attention would have been attracted by the chaos that characterises too many lounges in 'dementia care' homes. Large communal rooms, undifferentiated by little other than being places where people with dementia are taken to spend their time in the company of people with whom they may have little in common.

In the early months Peggy visited most days but as her arthritis worsened, probably aggravated by the stress of being separated from Spencer, she now only came on the days when she had some energy and when every movement wasn't accompanied by searing pain or gnawing discomfort. On those days Spencer would come alive. He was animated and his joy was etched across every line, furrow and wrinkle that splendidly marked the age of this kindly man. They would hold hands, there were smiles and Spencer would spontaneously reach out and grip Peggy's arm. It was closeness personified, borne out of years being together – as one.

So what had happened? Where did Spencer's new lease of life come from? Separated from Peggy he had always been quiet, passive, on the cusp of being withdrawn, and while Spencer's response to Peggy remained the same, it was his behaviour when they were away from each other that was transformed out of all recognition. Suddenly he had become jovial, aware, even curious. While you might imagine this would have pleased Peggy, who had always worried about how her husband was coping without her, his rediscovered passion for life actually horrified her. And it was not only Peggy who was aghast.

As soon as Gillian arrived at the home, she captured Spencer's attention and soon, it seemed, his heart as well. His chair in the lounge was forsaken within days and instead he would hover wherever staff had decided to sit Gillian. Never agitated but clearly loitering with intent, for if a chair next to her was vacated by a resident who had decided it was time to move on, he would be there if not in a flash, then as soon as his aged legs would allow. And from that point he was alive. He was animated, tactile and more than anything, clearly happy. It was as if Peggy had entered his life again, but given this hadn't happened, why was Gillian provoking such a response? She had a pleasing smile, a cheery face but in no way did she resemble Peggy.

Misinterpretations and misidentifications are at the

core of dementia, so why should anyone have been surprised by Spencer's behaviour? Sight loss and impaired facial recognition can undermine the capacity to perceive accurately, while both mind and memory can play tricks leading to errors of identification.

But Spencer was not misidentifying Gillian. This was not a man who was confused. This wasn't a man walking around with a woman *knowing* she was his wife when in truth she was a relative stranger. No this was Spencer being attentive and affectionate with a woman who he knew was *not* his wife. If you asked Spencer "Is this your wife?", he would unhesitatingly say "No", occasionally with a puzzled look on his face as if thinking, "Why have you asked such an absurd question?" Getting him to answer the question "Where's Peggy?" when he was in the company of Gillian was less easy, but if processing and language allowed he would say "Gone" or "Not sure" before being absorbed once more in the company of Gillian. This is what was upsetting Peggy and indeed Gillian's husband, Peter. Spencer and Gillian were happy because they were in each other's company. Two people wanting to be together, content when sharing time, yes one more attracted to the other, but the other clearly enjoying the attention too.

The need for intimacy is a basic human one intrinsic to our sense of self and wellbeing. Regardless of age and, significantly, regardless of dementia, people require the presence of someone they can be emotionally close to, even be affectionate with. In the care of people with dementia this need is often denied or ignored, for people wrongly believe that dementia diminishes the need for closeness, touch and affection. How wrong they are, and Spencer was demonstrating this was so. As was Gillian, for she reciprocated.

Yet dementia cannot be seen in a vacuum. It affects the lives of others. Peggy was devastated. When she visited, Spencer was hers but she knew most of the time his heart now belonged to someone else. She was bewildered. She felt betrayed. "How could Spencer be doing this to me? I know he's ill but this is cruel. Who would've thought this is how we'd end?"

I explained that Spencer's actions were not heartless, nor were they a true expression of infidelity. They were a consequence of his intellectual disability. His memory for events, even his own history, was in name only. Recent experiences were effaced within moments. He was living solely in the here and now. His feelings were reactive and detached from the objective reality of his life and hence he was no longer able to exercise judgement based on the knowledge that his life had an underpinning and enduring narrative. A narrative that would have given him a sense of belonging. A feeling of continuity. Instead, his thoughts, motivations and actions were like flotsam on the water, swept along by who or what was before him. And if in that moment the immediacy of life was unspeakably appalling then that was all life comprised (Stokes 2010). Although Spencer was lost, lonely and insecure, he had not lost his moral compass. Instead, this was about a man who needed to feel safe and wanted. So he and Gillian sat with each other, held hands and smiled at each other. And both were happy. Yes, if he had not been living with dementia he would have acted differently. Similarly if Peggy had not been living with arthritis she would have run upstairs. Both were trying to cope with the reality of their disability. It was just that Spencer's struggles were less easy to appreciate.

Peggy listened, she understood and for several weeks all was reasonably well. Each time she visited she tried not to ask how Spencer was for she knew guilt would be the inevitable emotion regardless of what she heard. She didn't want to hear he was quiet, keeping himself to himself, a little 'down', for time and again she would say, "If only I could get here more often." Yet nor did she want to hear how well he was doing for that meant Gillian was giving her husband solace and affection, and that she couldn't bear. But how dare she want her husband, who she treasured with all her heart to be anxious and sorrowful? Peggy could not win, yet she stoically soldiered on until one day Spencer crossed a line.

Peggy, Peter, his children, staff, visiting relatives were all to varying degrees tolerating the relationship that existed between Gillian and Spencer. All who were not emotionally involved would have been heartless not to have been touched by their affectionate ways, even when Spencer started to tenderly kiss Gillian on the cheek, but it wasn't to stop there.

Sexual need is common to all people. While it is not our cultural expectation, there is no age at which sexual interest and the capacity to enjoy sex are lost. Similarly people with dementia remain sexual beings like ourselves. And this is what Spencer started to express. However, for the first time Gillian did not reciprocate and Spencer did not possess the judgement and reasoning to desist.

As evenings approached, Spencer's amorous behaviour was triggered by any number of cues. Dusk, table lamps being switched on and residents reappearing in the lounge in their pyjamas and dressing gowns were probably conjuring up thoughts of bedtime and physical intimacy. He started to caress Gillian, fondle her breasts and play with her clothing. She would recoil and become fretful. There was no denying Gillian was now a vulnerable adult. Peter's disgust and anger could barely be contained. His children demanded Spencer be moved to another care home, or at the very least 'be given something'!

Gillian's care plan now required staff to separate them at the first sign of Spencer becoming aroused. However, as Spencer's behaviour was predictable, triggered by cues that tapped into remote emotional memories of impending nights of sex and affection, the logical solution was to separate them beforehand and accompany Gillian to her room where she could sit or even on occasions have an early night. However, such were the feelings Spencer had for Gillian she now constituted a fresh emotional memory trace and so out of sight was not out of mind. When separated he searched. Walking along hallways, in and out of others' bedrooms he was determined to find her. Never distressed or angry, for this was a man of gentle ways but everyone feared what would happen if he was to find her. And one evening he did.

Spencer was discovered standing by Gillian's bed staring down at her. To some it was a harmless intrusion. To a few it was a tender moment. To Peter and the children it was a threatening act that was beyond the pale. Peter stormed into the manager's office. "If you don't get him away from my wife, I'm involving the police. He's stalking her." But what could be done? There was no way Spencer could be confined. And nor was Gillian going to spend her time trapped in her room behind a locked or baffled door. Gillian's family had wondered whether he could 'be given something', that something being antipsychotic medication, but what would sedating Spencer do for his quality of life and possibly his physical welfare? For several years we have known that only a small minority of people with dementia derive benefit from treatment with antipsychotics. There are also health risks that can even result in death (Banerjee 2009). How about moving Spencer to another care home? But he was now seen as a predator – only one care home was prepared to accept him and that was seven miles away. So not only would a move be unsettling to Spencer, Peggy would be similarly affected for she was barely coping with one bus journey let alone the two that moving Spencer to this care home would involve.

Yet these 'solutions' represented old-style thinking: a culture of dementia care where feelings are denied, motivations ignored and managing is the limit of any therapeutic horizon. What if rather than managing Spencer's behaviour it was possible to support his need for closeness and intimacy, even if it fell short of sexual gratification? And there was a card to play. That card was Peggy, for there was never a time when she did not trump his feelings for Gillian. Spencer lived in the here and now and if in that moment Peggy was present then it was she who consumed his attention and feelings. After all, it had been known for years that as a couple Spencer and Peggy were as one.

Simulated Presence Therapy (SPT) was first described 20 years ago yet in no way can it be said to have moved into the foreground of person-centred interventions. The objective is to simulate the presence of a significant person to whom there is an emotional attachment and in turn calm, reassure and reduce distressed behaviours (Stokes 2008). While SPT may only work for a minority of people with dementia, might it be possible to simulate the presence of Peggy – not to soothe Spencer but, as evening encroached, to direct his affection and desire to the woman who meant more to him than anyone else.

Peggy would have agreed to nearly anything to have her Spencer back and bring to an end the febrile atmosphere and accusations that were causing her so much hurt. Over the next couple of weeks Peggy compiled a photograph album that stretched back more than 50 years. Photographs that captured the essence of their relationship and showed why Spencer remained captivated by his wife even in the midst of his dementia. Them windswept on a beach while they were courting. Peggy sitting on the bonnet of car that to this day she believes Spencer 'borrowed' from the garage he worked in to impress his fiancée. Their wedding day. Outside the hotel where they spent their first nights together on honeymoon. In their garden and on holiday. Peggy on special nights out and – Spencer's favourite photo – Peggy looking thoughtful as she gazed out of the window while on a coach trip to York. And as a finishing, personal and compelling touch, each page lightly sprinkled with Peggy's perfume.

I met with Peter and his children and explained that in their different ways both Spencer and Gillian were vulnerable, and while it was difficult for Peter to accept, during the day could we agree that both his wife and Spencer benefited from their tender companionship? There were cross words but Peter was a sensible and compassionate man who eventually admitted this was so. So rather than demand they be separated at all times might we focus on the evenings when Spencer was no longer a source of comfort to Gillian? With agreement secured, Spencer's care plan was to be as defined and prescribed as Gillian's. Whereas Gillian's was designed to meet her need for peace of mind and safety, Spencer's was also constructed to meet his needs, namely his need for intimacy and sexual satisfaction.

At the end of the day as soon as the decision was taken to accompany Gillian to the privacy of her room a carer would sit with Spencer and the pages of the album would be slowly turned. The imagery, the emotional memories and the scent of Peggy consumed Spencer as if it was his wife sitting next to him. Her presence had been simulated. He would sigh, touch, sometimes stroke photographs, and on occasions he would say "Look, Peggy"; often his words were unintelligible, but that did not matter. Every fibre of his being confirmed his love and desire for his wife. After a short period, probably no more than five minutes, Spencer would be left to gaze at his wife. Thereafter a carer would return every 30 minutes to sit with him and turn more pages. All interspersed with spontaneous meaningful moments as those who found themselves with 60 seconds or so to spare would spend time with Spencer 'and his wife'.

Who knows what thoughts, memories and emotions

were being provoked by the photographs that had been so meticulously assembled by Peggy, but Spencer's expression was joyful, and rarely did he place the album to one side to walk away. And if he did, it was never to seek out Gillian. Such was his cheery demeanour it was as if Peggy was his invisible companion as he contentedly walked the hallways. He no longer had any need for Gillian.

Yet on waking the following morning, such is the unforgiving nature of dementia, the previous evening's preoccupation with the allure of Peggy was forgotten and once more Gillian was the focus of his tenderness. For Spencer in the midst of his advanced dementia his life was once more rich in emotion. His days, evenings and possibly his dreams were now fulfilled and while there might be two women in his life nobody was in any doubt who it was who nestled deepest within his heart.

TWELVE

It is not death he feared

Walter was on his way again. Shuffling along on his bottom it was a spectacle no one wished to see. In many ways the strange manner in which he manoeuvred himself around the first floor dementia care unit where he had lived for the past 11 months defined his whole being. Invariably this was when people noticed him. It was what his carers responded to. The behaviours and incidents that resulted from his conduct were what families of other residents were complaining about. And there were many complaints. Some thought the way he became wedged in corners or in doorways was little better than neglect. Others were more concerned about his bruised fingers, while some saw him as simply being in the way as there had been trips and falls. But why was he doing it? Shuffling along took so much effort and while Walter said little he must have found it unbearably uncomfortable and exhausting. His shuffling endeavours rarely lasted more than a minute or two before he would stop, having reached no particular destination.

Walter was a thin, elderly man with a diagnosis of Binswanger's disease, a type of vascular dementia characterised by slowness, difficulty walking, poor bladder control and emotional ups and downs. His skin was pale, his face gaunt. His cheekbones were sharply defined, while his sunken eyes were framed by round-rimmed spectacles. He often seemed focused on something that nobody else could see. You would describe him as bookish for even though his dementia was now quite advanced he had the look of a studious man. As he hunched over his meal in the dining room, it looked for all the world as if he was poring over some dusty old manuscript.

He had been a college bursar who, following his retirement, had busied himself doing voluntary work for a number of local charities. A popular figure, he was respected by all who knew him. But that was a different time. Now widowed, living in a care home he had few visitors. The occasional old friend from his college days would drop by. A cousin he was once particularly close to visited but much less than she once did, so difficult did she find seeing him "being brought down by his dementia". Add a neighbour or two and these were the sum total remaining of his once active social circle. His daughters never visited but they were in contact with the care home most weeks enquiring about "the old man". A term of endearment: they were not alienated from their father, it was just that they both lived in New Zealand. His youngest had visited several times when she was in England on a business trip not long after Walter had come to live in the home and you could see how fond they were of each other. She had become quite upset during her final visit telling the home manager that she feared she would never see her father alive again and regretting that she and her sister lived so far away. However, nobody can construct their lives based on what can never be known, and how could his daughters have ever been aware that late in his life their father would be frail, alone and living with dementia? Equally how could anyone have known that as Walter's dementia progressed his behaviour would one day become extraordinarily bizarre?

Walter had arrived at the care home bemused, yet courteous. Unsteady on his feet, he needed a walking stick. Despite the stick he looked as if could lose his balance and fall in an instant. Accompanied by his cousin, Hilda, she confided that it had been "very sad seeing such an intelligent man become so inept". As Walter's intellectual faculties had diminished she had been given responsibility for all his affairs and when he admitted to her that he could no longer carry on living by himself it was Hilda who had chosen a care home for him. As she lovingly talked about Walter, who she felt was more like a brother than a cousin, she portrayed a proud and gentle man, one who would be no trouble at all. How wrong she was to be.

Walter slipped into the routines of the care home with ease and hence appeared to be adjusting quickly to his new life. Yet it was not all plain sailing, for his vascular dementia continued to progress. There were periods when he would be agitated, vacant and bewildered, possibly because he was experiencing transient ischaemic attacks, or more likely because he was having small strokes often referred to as 'strokelets'. Recovery was often incomplete and so in stops and starts Walter deteriorated, more physically than intellectually. As he became more dependent, accompanying Walter to the toilet or to his bedroom to change his clothes became a regular occurrence. However, he was now ponderous in his movements and so likely to fall as he tentatively placed one foot in front of another that two nurses had to assist him, and this took an age. A decision was taken. It was now best for Walter to be assisted using a wheelchair. It was certainly a more efficient way for Walter to be cared for. Risk of falls would be managed and time would not be lost accompanying him slowly along hallways and into rooms.

Days later Walter was discovered on the floor in the dining room. He hadn't fallen. He wasn't hurt. He had simply slid from his chair and settled on the floor half concealed by the table where a short time before he'd been eating his lunch. The following day it happened again. As before he was helped back into the chair, transferred to his wheelchair and taken to an armchair in the lounge. Walter's keyworker nurse spoke to the unit manager and his care plan was revised. Believing that Walter was no longer particularly comfortable or maybe at ease sitting at the dining table, once he had eaten his meal he was now to be taken to the lounge and sat in a comfy armchair.

Following the care plan to the letter, the next day, having eaten his meal, Walter was transferred to his wheelchair and taken to the lounge where he was settled in an armchair by the window so he could look out at the garden. And from the comfort of his chair he surreptitiously slid onto the floor! It was always to be the same. It didn't matter where he was sitting in the lounge, sometimes in a circle facing the television, sometimes in front of the glowing artificial fire, within minutes he would be on the floor. And he was not content to simply place himself on the floor because he would shuffle out of the room on his bottom to destinations unknown.

This was now to be the behaviour that summed up Walter. He would not only slide out of any chair in any room and shuffle away, he started to slide out of his bed. He perfected the art of slipping down from a chair or from his bed so not once did he injure himself, but shuffling on his bottom brought with it different consequences. He would manoeuvre himself with his arms outstretched and the flat of his palms on the floor. His exposed fingers would get trodden on by unwary residents, and sometimes he couldn't shuffle through doors fast enough: his fingers would become trapped as doors closed on him. Every now and then he found himself wedged between items of furniture. Sometimes his shuffling came to an end in the doorway of another resident's room who now found themselves trapped in their room by Walter's unwanted presence.

When found, he was invariably lifted into his wheelchair and taken to the lounge or his room where the pattern was destined to repeat itself. Remarkably, if nurses were slow transferring him from his wheelchair he would attempt to slide onto the floor and, if successful, would shuffle away. Slowly and painfully he would commence a journey which, if he had stayed in his wheelchair, could have been negotiated with much greater ease. But where did he wish to be? He never said. While his speech was sparse he could make some of his basic needs known, but his slipping, sliding and shuffling were enduring mysteries.

"Walter, why are you doing this, where do you want to go?" "I don't know. I don't know. I don't know."

Helping him up from the floor or extricating him from tight corners was habitually met with "No. No. Don't touch me".

Accompanied by a specialist dementia care nurse, I visited the home. After weeks of trying to understand Walter, the home manager's exasperation was obvious. There were too many complaints, the risk of injury to Walter and others was unacceptable and she feared it would soon be said that she was providing an unsafe care environment. And, in truth, for Walter this was already so. We tried to fathom why his behaviour had changed so dramatically. For months he had lived in the home without ever attempting to slide out of chairs, let alone shuffle away. Equally it wasn't as if, in the beginning, he slid out of a chair and shuffled away once in a while, and only with the passage of time had episodes become more and more frequent. No, the onset been abrupt, and his actions were from the start were incessant and his determination unwavering. We were at a loss.

We took a break and I went into the corridor and by chance there was Walter sliding out of his wheelchair in the hallway outside the toilet. I walked over and saw the nurse had not taken Walter into the toilet because whoever had used the toilet previously had strewn toilet paper, some of it soiled, over the floor and she was clearing it away. Having slid onto the floor Walter didn't shuffle away but instead he attempted to enter the toilet. Unless he had been in desperate need, and he wasn't for the nurse told me he had already soiled himself, his behaviour was counterintuitive. Why would Walter commit effort to an endeavour that would take an inordinate amount of time when, if he had waited a few moments longer, he would have been wheeled into the toilet with neither exertion nor risk? It wasn't as if he couldn't see the nurse and what she was doing for the door remained wide open and she was in full view. However, could it be that he had no insight or capacity to reason? This was possible for Walter's dementia was advancing, but the cause of his dementia was vascular in origin, and in vascular dementia intellectual deterioration is patchy and insight can be better preserved than is seen for example in Alzheimer's disease. I had also been told that Walter understood a lot that was said to him and was still able to communicate some of his care needs. The conundrum remained as perplexing as ever.

I returned to the unit's sitting room where we were meeting and found we had been joined by the unit manager. A delightful woman, Jo was passionate, caring and fretting more than most over Walter's plight for she felt she was failing him. I explained what I'd just seen and she said that wasn't uncommon. It seemed to her that Walter would take any opportunity he could to extricate himself from the wheelchair even if it was to his disadvantage. I suggested we listed all we knew about Walter to see if we could uncover anything that might start to explain why he may be acting in such a bizarre way.

We agreed he was highly dependent and vulnerable to falling. He had been an intelligent man, described as proud. For months he had lived well on the unit until he suddenly stopped wanting to sit in chairs and had started at the same time to propel himself around the unit on his bottom. Neither pain nor discomfort were disincentives. And these behaviours started days after a wheelchair had been introduced to manage his care needs better and reduce the risk of falls. "It's the wheelchair. That has to be the explanation," I said, with no knowledge as to why, other than the fact this was the only aspect of his life that had changed and not one which could really be dismissed as coincidence. But if the wheelchair was the trigger, why was it?

Jo slipped out and returned with Walter's folder of case notes and documents. Flicking through the reams of daily diary entries she wanted to see how many days after he began to use the wheelchair that Walter's behaviour changed. As the rest of us talked Jo announced "Five days", and she began to take a letter out of a beige envelope across which was written in spidery handwriting, 'To Whom It May Concern'. "Oh, my word!" Jo exclaimed, passing to me a single sheet of writing paper.

An advanced directive is a legal document that allows a person to spell out their end-of-life care wishes ahead of time. This wasn't such a document but it might as well have been. Dated nearly a year before he came to live in the care home Walter had written: *"I dread the prospect of this wretched illness. Destroying my brain, dementia is taking away who I am and all I know. My girls, people, places, my contribution to the lives of others. What is life if not remembered?... Death I do not dread. If truth be told this is the answer, my solution, for I fear disability and degradation more than death itself."*

Walter had never resisted personal care but his body language had always revealed he did not welcome it either. It had always been felt by some nurses that he got himself into difficulties such as when cutting up his food, getting out of bed in the morning or delaying getting out of a chair when he needed the toilet because he didn't want to be helped. He never complained when help was offered, it was just that he did his best to avoid it. He was, as his cousin Hilda had described, a proud man, not pompous or conceited simply a man who throughout his life had been respected for who he was and what he did.

Neither the home manager nor Jo could remember how the 'letter' had found its way into the case notes although Jo had a vague recollection that she had been told Hilda had handed a letter to one of the nurses not long after Walter's arrival. Mistakes happen, even though we wish they didn't, and it had been filed unopened. Would it have made a difference if its contents had been known? I doubt it, for Walter's care had always been compassionate and sensitive, and it was only when his vulnerability became great had a course of action been inadvertently taken that had sadly exercised a detrimental effect on his emotional welfare.

As dependency and frailty closed in on him it was as if the wheelchair was seen by Walter as the symbol of his reliance on others, emblematic of his descent into puerile dependency and it was to be avoided at all costs, even if his determination to be independent of others led to the very humiliation he wished to avoid. So he slid out of chairs before he could be transferred into the wheelchair and he manoeuvred himself the only way he could. Fatigue, discomfort and pain were preferred to the ignominy of being seen as disabled. Perverse, yes, but the human will is both indomitable and so often mysterious to others.

THIRTEEN

The hurt ran deep

The science of psychology has, over the past 30 years, helped us better understand people with dementia, particularly those who are distressed or act in ways that are challenging to their carers. It has transformed what were once seen as symptoms of disease into an appreciation that emotions and behaviour which appear meaningless and without foundation in fact resonate with meaning, reflecting who the person with dementia is and what they want.

Behavioural analysis, sometimes known as ABC analysis, entered the field of caring for people with advanced dementia in the mid-1980s (Stokes 2000). The method requires the distressed or 'challenging' *behaviour* to be clearly described and recorded ('B') and then be placed in the context of the events that immediately preceded it (*antecedents* 'A') and the actions that directly followed (*consequences* 'C'). When combined with the time of day the behaviour occurred, the recordings may reveal what could be triggering or influencing it.

Behavioural analysis enables us to answer the questions what, where and when, but not why. Although the principles of behavioural analysis are straightforward, life and people rarely are so. In order to address this complexity, *functional analysis* builds on what is observed and asks *why* might the person act in this way when they find themselves in that situation at that time of day with those people. It examines the meaning or purpose the behaviour might have for the person – in other words, what is the function served by the behaviour? What might it say about who the person is and how they want to live their life? When we extend our analysis to embrace these highly individual influences we might find out, for example, that the behaviour is a person's way of coping with unhappiness, boredom or stress (as in the story of Elsie in chapter 10).

Interventions using behavioural analysis and functional analysis-based interventions have helped us to understand and reduce the distress of people with dementia, as well as assisting carers to cope with and even resolve a host of behaviours that challenge (Moniz-Cook *et al* 2001, Moniz-Cook *et al* 2003, James 2011). Yet as Alan was to prove there is little in life that is guaranteed.

One word summed up Alan: unpredictable. He would get worked up and angry for no obvious reason. Apparently where he was and who he was with had no bearing on how he behaved. He might be in the lounge, the sitting room or the office. He could be alone or with others, it seemingly did not matter. Nor was there any build up. You couldn't tell his mood was about to change.

One moment he would be fine, even happy, the next furious. Unfortunately, there was no point asking Alan why because his dementia was so severe words were beyond him.

I was asked to visit him in the care home where he lived not because the nurses and carers couldn't cope with his behaviour and distress, for he was easily consoled, but because Alan's wife was struggling to cope. Gwen couldn't bear hearing about how her husband could become so enraged. "It's not him," she would say, "He was such a quiet, gentle man."

Kate is one of the most able, passionate and compassionate home managers I have ever had the privilege to work with. She had already got her staff thinking about what might be causing Alan to get so upset, but they had come up with nothing. This had baffled Kate for she had long left behind the belief that dementia explained all. "There has to be a reason, but I can't work it out."

No one believed Alan's outbursts were due to the type of man he was, for his wife was adamant that her husband was one of the most placid, sweetest men you could have ever met: "Sometimes I wish he had stood up for himself more, but that wasn't him." A few staff had started to wonder whether it was because of his dementia, and Alan's wife had been heard saying "This bloody dementia has taken my Alan". However, it clearly hadn't. This was about the man, not his disease. He was reacting to something, but what? While his fits of temper were impulsive and extreme he was not disinhibited, as one nurse asked me. Disinhibition, arising from damage to the frontal part of the brain, means emotions are not only poorly restrained but the accompanying impulsive behaviours are frequent. Alan had had flurries of distressing and unintelligible outbursts, but in the main they happened every now and then. And when they did they were inexplicable.

I asked Kate if we could introduce a period of behavioural analysis. Her look betrayed that she wasn't keen. She knew it would be time-consuming and it would need each and every one of her staff to be on board, and not all were as passionate as she was to go that extra mile. But: "What else can we do?" I asked, "It's been an age and you're still totally nonplussed." Kate smiled and agreed.

I knew the period of analysis was likely to be lengthy, for in the main Alan's outbursts were infrequent and we needed to find out whether there was a pattern. The risk was that staff would lose enthusiasm and interest, and our attempts to understand Alan's behaviour would slowly unravel. However, I need not have been concerned. Kate rose to the challenge and was her normal brilliant self. She made sure her team didn't forget what was expected of them, asking for updates at staff handovers and weekly resident review meetings, and reminding them to always complete the ABC chart as soon as possible after an incident. Kate had already fostered a culture of curiosity and enquiry, a culture that characterises the best care homes. Seeking answers to questions was the way Kate and her team worked and we now built on this state of 'organisational readiness' to elevate the performance of her staff to hopefully help alleviate both Alan's and Gwen's suffering.

The period of systematic observation and recording started and seven weeks later it had yielded nothing! In that time Alan had worked himself into a state on 12 occasions and, as everyone already knew, there was no pattern. Yes, staff consistently responded with patience and calmness (C). They gave him time, would smile and chat to him, and as such he was easily soothed. But that wasn't why he was becoming upset. He wasn't acting this way to get these rewards for this is how staff always were with him. And anyway, how could Alan be so manipulative? He couldn't remember from one moment to the next so how would he have been able to remember that if he acted in a certain way he would get the reactions he wanted? Sadly, it is so naive when carers and unfortunately even professional practitioners say people with advanced dementia are being calculating or attention-seeking for this is an intellectual impossibility in the relative absence of memory and reasoning.

As for the time of day, location, activity, and the actions and presence of others at the times Alan became upset (A), the information was all over the place. It didn't matter what was happening or where Alan was, on occasions he would just 'go off on one'. So with no pattern, we couldn't even attempt to go down the path of functional analysis for to do so would mean trying to explain why people in general, or Alan in particular, act in unpredictable ways for no obvious reason.

We were all dispirited but I asked Kate if I could speak to the team because I had a suggestion. While behavioural analysis had revealed nothing that could help Alan I wanted to talk to them about another way of working that might give us some fresh insights, and that new way of working was *appreciative inquiry*.

Appreciative inquiry comes from the world of organisational psychology. It is an approach that looks *not* at what is wrong or broken, but instead looks at what is working well and is successful. And its principles can be of great help when trying to understand why people with severe dementia present with complex behaviours.

Unlike behavioural and functional analysis, appreciative inquiry disregards the person's distress and focuses instead on the positive, such as when the person is happy, content and relaxed and inquires about these times. Immediately this transforms the nature and tone of the investigation. Rather than staff being questioned about unwanted behaviours and emotions, with the expressed or implicit undertone that they could have done better, instead the inquiry focuses on the times when all is well. Occasions when carers are potentially doing the right thing and life is how the person with dementia wants it to be. If these positive situations could be better understood and encouraged to happen more often then the frequency of the unwanted behaviour would inevitably diminish.

As I had hoped, this new approach resonated with Kate's staff and we soon established the situations where Alan had *never* showed signs of distress. Never when in the company of his wife. Helping with his personal care, regardless of how intimate, was always accepted without any fuss. He had never become upset while in his own room, whether in bed or sitting in his chair gazing into the garden, or when carers had popped in to see him, not even when other residents had inadvertently walked in. Nor had he ever got worked up at mealtimes, not even when others had taken food off his plate or residents had squabbled among themselves. Nor had there ever been an incident in the hallways. So was this because at these times and in these settings Alan was at peace with himself and his surroundings? He could have been preoccupied with his own thoughts, distracted by activity, had a sense of security when he was in his room surrounded by his familiar possessions, or been reassured when in the company of people he could identify with, especially his wife and carers. The answer had to be yes and no. Yes, because appreciative inquiry had provided evidence that could be interpreted as such but also no, for Alan had flared when talking to staff and while busying himself when in the lounge, the small sitting room, the office and in the 'pub' that had been created in what had once been an activities room. Hence preoccupation, occupation and company were clearly not sufficient conditions to prevent Alan's mood dramatically deteriorating. But it also could not be said that the rooms where Alan became upset possessed the necessary conditions to bring about a deterioration in his mood for most of the time in these places Alan would be his normal placid self.

However might it be that he was not at peace with himself in these places at particular times because something or someone happened to make him feel insecure? Something out of the ordinary or maybe somebody was present who was rarely there, which more than likely would mean a visitor. And what or whoever it was only appeared in certain parts of the home, the ones where Alan became distressed.

I looked at the ABC charts. Unfortunately while they had been completed sometimes the detail was sparse so it wasn't always possible to get a true picture about what had happened – "Sitting with Alan" (A), "He was standing in the lounge. By himself." (A), "We were talking. Had been for a while and then he changed. Angry and upset." (A and B), "I tried to calm him down."(C), "He walked off and I followed him. Went to his room and was okay." (C). All useful information but more would have been better. However, what I could glean was that there was a number of different staff involved so Alan's behaviour was not triggered by any one person in particular, although there remained the possibility that there could have been a resident or visitor in the background who had not been noticed.

I walked around the home. I lingered. I sat in all the places where Alan became distressed to see if there was anything I could see or hear that was common to all. There was nothing. This didn't surprise me because whatever I needed to find was only seldom present. This was going to be a lengthy inquiry.

The smell of paint as I walked through reception was palpable. The refurbishment that had been underway for the past few weeks was to everyone's delight all but finished. The home looked fresh and clean, uplifted by new curtains and carpets as well as a brand new colour scheme. The upheaval staff had had to cope with while preserving a sense of normality had been worthwhile.

Kate was in the lounge. She was her usual ebullient self, but also the purveyor of unfortunate tidings. Alan had become worked up yesterday and this time it hadn't been so easy to calm him down. And for the first time he had become enraged in the hallway. I looked at the ABC chart. Alan had been incensed outside the lounge screaming incoherently and pointing at a picture. I spoke to Mandy, one of the care assistants who had tried to walk him away. "I've never seen him like it. You couldn't understand a word, but you could tell how angry he was. Furious. It was crazy." But why had he not reacted like this before? He must have passed the picture hundreds of times. "No he hadn't," said Mandy, "He'd never seen it before. It was only put up yesterday. It's one of the pictures of the town we got as part of the new decoration. You know, one of them nostalgia photos."

A photo from the 1960s. Just off market square at the end of the high street. I recognised the building although fifty years ago it looked far grander than the faded facade of today's George Hotel. So assuming it was the photograph, what was it about the George Hotel that caused Alan to get in such a state? And whatever it was, how did it relate to all the previous episodes?

Standing with Gwen I asked her what might it be about this photograph of the George Hotel that could have so upset her husband? She didn't hesitate. "It's not the hotel, Graham. It's the place next door. That's the old head office of The Echo. It's the newspaper Alan used to work for."

Alan had been a local reporter. He had never strayed far from his roots and had always worked for The Evening Echo. Having completed his National Service in 1956 he got a job at the newspaper as, in the words of Gwen "a glorified office boy". One early winter morning a few months after starting he was asked if he could cover a speedway fixture as the paper's sports reporter was going to be reporting on a football match that evening, the big one, a local derby against City. His piece was well-received and he was asked to do more and more reporting, both sport and news. And that's how it happened. No great ambition coming to fruition. No culmination to years of training and apprenticeship. Alan just sort of became a reporter. And he loved it. He was proud of his town and he felt being a reporter allowed him not only to restore the pride of the local communities he reported on, but he could also damn with faint praise those who he felt were tearing the soul out of a once prosperous town, as well as condemning ("blame and shame" was Gwen's view) the miscreants who were literally and metaphorically damaging the area's reputation.

Years passed, times changed and Alan the reporter became Alan the office manager. Not that he wanted to be. But a new editor, elevated with the praise of the newspaper's owner ringing in his ears, flushed with ambition and full of ideas to build up the readership, felt that Alan was too 'old-school'. His values were no longer those of today. Stories he wanted to write, events he wanted to cover, were no longer seen as the ones people wanted to read or know about. His articles and reports became more and more occasional, and when his name did appear beneath a headline what he had written was brief to the point of being anonymous. The writing was on the wall and so when he was offered a back-office role he knew he had no choice but to accept.

Unfortunately sitting behind a desk all day organising the work schedules of others wasn't for him. At 61 his world had been turned upside down. Yet very soon his concerns were to be of no consequence.

Alan was set in his ways and his values may now have been those from another time but his heart had never been anywhere other than in the right place. He was an exceedingly likeable man who got on with everyone, so to be accused of sexual harassment and lewd behaviour was beyond belief. But he had and his 'victim' wanted retribution.

The paper's owner, whose family had owned The Echo since the 1920s, was well-connected, and liked nothing better than letting it be known that his friends included the 'great and good', one of whom had asked if his daughter could have some work experience at the newspaper while she considered her options. Options that seemed to veer between unrealistic ambitions to work in fashion, with less emphasis on work and more on fashion, and doing little other than enjoy a spoilt and pampered lifestyle. Keen to please his influential friend, who as an aside was a significant contributor to The Echo's advertising revenue, the answer was an unequivocal yes.

With hindsight 'working' for Alan was always going to end badly. To him the attitudes of a teenager who in Gwen's words was "a spoilt brat" were an anathema. Alan commented about her manner and how disrespect-ful she was but was simply told to be more tolerant. He tried. He did his best and kept his own counsel. He tried to be more appreciative of her, but: "She was impossible. Even the most reasonable request would set her off."

It was an ordinary day in the office, another one to be

endured. Alan had only been in the building a few minutes when he was beckoned into the boardroom where he was summarily sacked by an incandescent editor who was clearly concerned for his own future. The girl had accused Alan of inappropriate behaviour when he had asked her to stay late one evening. She also said that Alan has been making suggestive comments when no one else was around. Her father was outraged and demanded Alan be dismissed and, if he was not, he would make sure that The Echo got no more business from him and do his utmost to savage the reputation of the paper's owner.

Needless to say while nobody at the paper believed there was a shred of truth in the accusations the outcome was inevitable. Alan pleaded his case but he loved the paper and he knew the consequences if he protested his innocence and demanded that the girl's allegations be challenged and investigated. He felt he had no choice. He meekly accepted the decision, even though inwardly he was heartbroken. He was comforted that his colleagues, some of whom he counted as friends, were to be told that that he had been made redundant. He was grateful to be told that he would get redundancy pay and it was reassuring knowing that he wasn't too far off retirement, even though he had no idea how he and Gwen would manage for the next few years. But they did. He got himself a part-time job in a supermarket. He remained the same amiable man, his forgiving nature tempering any resentment he may have felt, but Gwen knew he had been deeply hurt.

So that was why Alan had become enraged when he saw the photograph – but how did this relate to all the other outbursts? Or was there no relationship, and I was hoping for a connection that didn't exist?

He had never flared in the hallways until now. Never during personal care in the bathroom or in his en suite. Never in his room, nor at mealtimes. But what might the communal rooms where Alan did occasionally flare now share in common with the hallway where the picture hung. I went to the office. I walked into the 'pub', into the sitting room, and saw nothing that might constitute a connection. Now on to the lounge, but I never arrived. As I walked past the ladies' hairdressing salon there was a lady waiting for her hair to be done. She was gazing at a magazine, one the hairdresser had given her. She couldn't read but she was engrossed, turning pages, pausing at times to take in a photograph or two. And on the table next to the pile of magazines was a newspaper. The Echo!

I looked at the ABC charts and one entry said "Alan sitting in lounge. Sat down with him. No problems. He smiled. Was talking to him. Showed him the newspaper (A). Started yelling at me. He stood up. Very, very worked up (B). Stormed out of lounge (C)."

Two members of staff who had recorded Alan's fury at other times were on duty but in their ABC entries neither had mentioned a newspaper. One couldn't remember if Alan might have been holding one. She had come into the lounge having heard him screaming out and all she could recall was him standing by the television shouting and "kind of shaking". However, the other staff member, Iffat, was certain that on the bar in the 'pub' where she was running a reminiscence group, there was a newspaper.

Alan had walked in and spontaneously 'gone off on one'. But how could she remember such a minor detail? She could because Kate had been walking the home to check all was well and as she left the pub she said to Iffat, "I've put the Echo over there. Your gentlemen might find something interesting in it to talk about. There's something about Wanderers' players from the past."

Yet if Alan's mood swings were to do with seeing the newspaper, a newspaper that provoked awful memories and upsetting feelings, why did it happen so occasionally? The Echo came out every evening, although to be honest I could barely recall seeing copies lying around the home.

Kate was mortified. "Are you saying it's me who's responsible for Alan behaving like he does? I'm to blame for all his months of torment?" There was no doubt that this was what I was saying, although of course it was not intentional.

Kate would on occasions work the odd night shift, or sometimes just come back to do a few hours in the evening, especially if there were staff shortages. She liked to stay close to the life of her home and what better way was there than rolling up her sleeves and doing what deep down she loved best, caring for her aged residents? When she was due to do a few hours in the evening or a night shift she'd go home early afternoon, have a few hours' rest and back she'd come pleased once more to be wearing her nurse's uniform. And she would always return by bus because years ago she'd been involved in a car accident, one that had profoundly affected her. Not so much because of her injuries, even though these had been quite serious, but because the driver of the car that crashed into her in a queue of traffic had fallen asleep at the wheel. Ever since then Kate would never drive if she felt she too might be driving while tired and exhausted. That's why having worked most of the day already, and knowing she would be going home late at night or the following morning it was common sense for her to travel by bus. And to pass the time she would buy the Evening Echo to read, which would then be left on whichever unit she was working on for the residents to read, look at or possibly for staff to use when prompting conversations with them, which meant at times one would appear on the unit where Alan lived.

Kate asked how I could be sure and I said I was because as soon as I thought we had the answer I tracked down a copy of the Evening Echo and placed it in Alan's room, on his armchair. I found Alan and together we strolled in the garden before I guided him to his room. We walked in and as he approached his chair his mood immediately darkened and this genial man started to gesticulate and swear at the newspaper. Ready for this I grabbed it and, apologising for it being in his room, I literally tossed the newspaper into the hallway. We no longer had a mystery to solve. A moment's upset to put to an end to a distressing conundrum had been a price worth paying. Down came the photograph, the Evening Echo was 'banned'. Now spared the upsetting reminder of a wretched injustice, Alan could once more be the unfailingly pleasant and inoffensive man he had always been. Analysis and inquiry had together yielded rich pickings.

FOURTEEN

Scared of life: 'twas ever thus

I look at you sitting there and I'm trying to picture you aged three, holding the hand of a man you don't know, staring at a chair where your mother should be. What would you be thinking?

In her room again. Never coming out, Shirley was again causing concern. Isolated, wafer-thin, her haunted expression, her fretted eyes betrayed the depths of her foreboding. But why? Shirley was frightened, yet not frightened of this, or scared of that. Just frightened. That is unless she was in her room, when her anxious demeanour calmed. Yet never so soothed that you would say sitting alone made her happy or even truly calm for her fingers were still restless, worrying her hem or picking at whatever might be in reach. Which is why her carers were concerned. Was there no way her life in the care home could be more pleasurable? All they were being told was Shirley needed bringing out of herself and being left alone in her room was not the answer.

Occasionally staff tried to coax her out of her room but she would invariably recoil and often lash out. At such times some were frightened of her, especially the younger ones, and they would vilify her. But it was clear she was more frightened of them than they should ever have been of her. And at such times they really were not seeing Shirley. Instead they saw dementia for this was now her life's destination. There was nothing other than dementia. Just nothing. It represented the absence of Shirley. She had disappeared beneath the sum of forgetfulness, incoherent speech and unwanted behaviours. We may call this 'diagnostic overshadowing', but this meant little to them, so I simply said, "You're not seeing Shirley. You're caring, but do you care?"

Three months had passed since Shirley had left her neat, yet cluttered terraced house to enter the care home. While in the months building up to her admission her house had mirrored her own dilapidated state, this is not how it had once been. Cluttered yes, untidy no. All around, on shelves, in glass cabinets, in fact on every surface Shirley could find she had surrounded herself with crockery, china, ornaments and all manner of collectables. Everything was meticulously and lovingly cared for. However, conspicuous by their absence were holiday mementoes. There were none, because there had been no holidays to remember.

Young to have been diagnosed with probable Alzheimer's disease, Shirley was still only 69 years old but perplexingly she looked both young and old for her age. While her withered frame and sunken cheeks had aged her, her skin betrayed few signs of ageing. Without knowledge it was difficult to say how old Shirley was. If anyone had bothered to ask they probably would have said between 60 and 80!

Her dementia probably started a decade ago, not certainly, because it was only on reflection that Shirley's family guessed at this. For quite some time they did not realise that anything was wrong. How could they have done? Shirley did so little, and never anything that was unexpected. And she rarely ventured out. Instead her life was dominated by routines and habits all lived out within the confines of her house and garden. And, as we know, people with dementia, in familiar surroundings, in the midst of engrained habits and time-honoured routines, can perform as well as ever for several years because learning and reasoning, the very aspects of memory and thinking that are damaged early in Alzheimer's disease, are barely required. In other words what needs to be done to get safely on with life is done almost automatically. So Shirley's sheltered and predictable existence meant she was able to both deceive herself and others that all was well. That was until the familiar became shrouded in mystery as more and more of her memories and ways of being were eroded and her secure existence was thrown into chaos.

As her home became less familiar and more threatening, Shirley retreated into herself and her world shrank to a three-foot square space wherein she sat, next to the gas fire opposite her television that would be on morning, noon and night with no heed paid to what was showing.

Before dementia took hold, her son used to visit twice a week to drop off the food shopping and deliver anything else his mother asked for or he thought she needed. It had been this way ever since Dad had died of a heart attack a few years before, leaving Mum to fend for herself. It was only after his father died that he and his sister realised how much their father had done to support their mother and maintain a semblance of normality. They had always known he was fiercely loyal and protective, making excuses when plans to go out were cancelled or when only he turned up for a day out with the grandchildren. Their plans to move house never came to fruition even though he was desperate to move. It was their garden; it was never big enough to accommodate his passion for roses and growing vegetables. But while Shirley would join in the fun of contemplating a future resonating with change and fulfilled dreams, or more accurately the fulfilment of her husband's dreams, all were destined to remain within the pages of magazines, brochures and estate agents' windows. Shirley was going nowhere. So they lived in increasingly cramped, or you might say cosy, circumstances as Shirley gathered her world around her. But why did she act this way?

Shirley rarely went out because 'out' was frightening. She would panic. She was terrified not because of what she would face, but because of what she had left behind. The security, the familiarity of her home. Hence change was similarly feared. Home was where she felt safe; a home that for Shirley was her world. Within four walls she lived her life. Her children were photographs and telephone calls, not visits and trips out together. Outside was a world she did not want to belong in. Shirley, while never formally diagnosed, was agoraphobic.

If Shirley could not contemplate going out as part and parcel of daily life then holidays were never going to happen. And as with so with so many things she lived vicariously. Through magazines and television, this was her contact with the outside world. So when Frank died it was understandable that she withdrew even more into her 'make-believe' world. The man she had relied upon for over 35 years was gone, she was alone and her need for security, the reassurance the familiar brought her, was felt even more acutely.

But as dementia took hold and wrestled familiarity from Shirley, her home lost its meaning. And as Shirley's emotions spiralled downwards, the demands of caring became impossible for her children. As she became more and more withdrawn, and did less and less for herself, their fondness faded, and worry and exasperation came to the fore. "Mum's miserable. She's scared. We're at our wits' end and in all honesty we can't take any more," was how her family saw it.

As her children despaired, plans were made for Shirley to move into a care home. A transition that, given Shirley's history, was always going to be extremely distressing. So it turned out to be. From the moment she arrived, lost and bewildered, she was agitated. She would never settle in the lounge. Never participate in any activities. And she would refuse to sit in the dining room. Pacing the corridors, refusing to eat, her weight loss was profound. While some respite was to be found if she was left to sit in her room it was understandable when one day her daughter asked, "Why are we prolonging Mum's unhappy, pointless life?"

But yet what had been Shirley's life? To a greater or lesser extent it had been her things. Not people, not places, not joining in activities or going to events, not anything other than the detritus she had gathered around her. She had invested her life in objects. And that's what needed to happen once more. The pleasure of her things needed to be reclaimed.

On her arrival at the care home Shirley's children had asked whether their mum could bring in some of her possessions to make her room homely and had been told of course she could. In truth the manager's words were ambiguous: while she had said yes, she had also advised that it shouldn't be anything too valuable as "things go missing". Also, keeping her room clean and tidy would be easier if it wasn't too cluttered. But cluttered and home were to Shirley synonymous. However having heeded the home manager's words, Shirley's room resembled a neat and soulless hotel room with just a few keepsakes dotted around to break the monotony. Probably somewhere nice to stay for a while, but not a place to live in. Without her clutter on view no wonder Shirley was never really calm, let alone happy.

I said to Shirley's daughter that while 'homely' could be achieved by curtains, wallpaper and cushions, fabrics and furniture cannot make a home. Home is where you feel safe, relaxed and, importantly, it's where you feel you belong. You have an affinity with all that is around because what you see is yours. Your things that resonate with memory and emotion. And in her mother's case this was even more so because what Shirley had surrounded herself with did not represent or remind her of her life – it was her life.

The pursuit of tidiness could not supersede Shirley's need for familiarity and reassurance, and while the risk of possessions going missing is real it is not as if precautions could not be taken and risks minimised. Shirley would be in her room much of the time watching over her things; her door could be closed, her glass display cabinet could be locked, shelves could be placed high, and her personal 'chest' – which residents' families were encouraged to fill with treasured things, yet which was curiously 'hidden' away in the wardrobe – could be brought out at supervised times for her to experience meaningful moments of activity.

Shirley's house had yet to be sold but already some of her bric-a-brac had been tidied away or disposed of because, as Shirley's dementia progressed, there had been inevitable breakages. Her lack of hygiene had also become an issue as faeces-encrusted hands left an unsavoury residue. However, a lot still remained, and much now reappeared in Shirley's room. To unknowing eyes the room became messy and cluttered, but to Shirley it was home.

Staff were asked to visit Shirley in her room everyday and spend time with her while she explored her 'treasure chest'. Let her take out whatever she wished and encourage her to place it all on a tray in front of her, and for the first time sitting among her clutter, gazing, touching and holding her things you could see she was content. As she rummaged through her treasures, in the middle of the tray she nearly always placed a photograph. A photograph of a young girl; angelic with blonde curls, a cheeky smile and wearing her finest dress. On the back, in faded print was written K W Wilson, Studio Portrait

Photographer, 14 February 1942. This photo captivated Shirley for this was one with a heart-rending story.

Behind a curtain, Kenneth Wilson had posed the little girl on a stool and, when all was perfect, the camera bulb flashed and the portrait was taken. Clambering down, the photographer took her hand, pulled back the curtain and Shirley skipped into the shop to be greeted by - no one. For the chair that minutes earlier had been occupied by Shirley's mother was empty. Shirley's mother, aged 19 years, unmarried and unable to carry the burden of parenthood any longer had gone, leaving behind her daughter, aged just three.

Shirley never saw her mother again. Though she was brought up by her loving grandmother is it any wonder that from that day Shirley craved security, rarely trusted anyone, sought sanctuary in what she could control and as soon as she could, married, set up home and thereafter rarely strayed from the safe confines she constructed for herself? Once that safety had been her house; now, with the help of her children, it was to be her room.

PART V

Touching lives

"Never believe that a few caring people can't change the world. For, indeed, that's all who ever have"
– MARGARET MEAD

FIFTEEN

The wrong question

Dan had been crying for days, ever since his wife had gone into hospital. Yet this wasn't why he was crying, for he did not know. His carers would say: "Dan, Connie isn't well. She's in hospital for a few days." He would look at them with a mixture of puzzlement and disbelief, for while he understood much of what they said his expression conveyed what he felt: "It cannot be true." But as he stood there mystified, the quizzical look would slowly disappear, for within seconds the words of others, more baffling than reassuring, had started to fade. Within a minute or so, all that had been said had *not* been forgotten, though. Why not forgotten? Because so profound was Dan's dementia no memory trace had been laid down, and so to him no words had been spoken in the first place. Only then, maybe now sitting in a chair, staring out of a window or walking a corridor would he start to cry. Upset, not because his wife was unwell but because she was absent, and her absence weighed heavy. Inexplicably, unbearably apart, it was into this emotional void Dan cried.

Dan and Connie had been married for 58 years and all who knew them understood that Dan, a great striding Aussie bull of a man, over six feet tall, more than 15 stone who had confidently chuckled his way through life was beholden to his wife. Connie was the woman he admired, respected and loved to the point of being all but dependent on her. And him, a strapping, fearless firefighter!

In turn Connie knew the love of a man who was devoted to her. A man who would do all that was humanly possible to make his wife happy and feel protected, and who had never lost the desire to prove to her that she had made the right decision when in 1951 she had surprised her parents and chosen Dan from the host of far more refined, eloquent and prosperous young men who had pursued the attractive and petite Connie Ryan.

They had two sons, Don and Greg, who both knew that Mum was the power within the house. Yes, Dad was full of bluster and he never failed to stand up for his wife and boys, but it was Mum who in tough times was the emotionally strong one. Full of common sense, rarely seduced by good fortune, but also never demoralised by adversity (she would even sometimes recite the words of Rudyard Kipling when she felt others were getting carried away by those twin imposters 'triumph and disaster') she always seemed to know what to say or do to make you see sense. Such as when it came to putting Dan back onto an even keel when it was time for him to retire as a firefighter and he thought he had become 'less of a man', or when he was diagnosed with prostate cancer and he was certain it was a death sentence.

In his heart of hearts Dan knew that without Connie his life would mean little. He was fretful and always fearing the worst; she was his rock. And Connie knew this as well. When Dan was diagnosed with dementia she, as her sons and friends would have anticipated, took it in her stride. She knew it would be a hard road. "If you ever need anything, anything at all, we'll be there for you," was what she heard from friends and family alike. But she was resourceful. She coped. She got on with things. She did her best but eventually she had to admit she just didn't have the energy to go on any longer. Dan would do such silly things. "He's a big, brawny child without a shred of common sense," she would say in her exasperated moments.

In truth the strain had started quite early as dementia took a hold on Dan's ability to remember. He would ask over and over again was she alright, where was she going, where had she been? Then the following and searching started. He just couldn't cope being away from Connie such was his need for her presence. Slowly it sucked the life out of her. She had no time for herself; just getting on with the chores of everyday life became an insuperable challenge because Dan was always there hovering and questioning. Their sons did their best, but while swapping stories and reminiscing helped, as did the odd fishing trip, it was Connie he wanted to be with. So when the time came for Dan to live in a care home there was only one decision to take. She was going as well. Not *had* to go, but *wanting* to, because in her own way she also needed him.

Initially the boys were aghast. Mum needed her life back. She needed to rest, have fun again. She couldn't keep on caring. They knew Dad needed her but now it was time for Mum to think of herself. But she was doing exactly that. And once they appreciated that looking after Dad would now be the responsibility of the carers who would be there 24/7 and Connie need only do what she wished to, when she wanted to, they knew that for their parents, living apart was not an option. The social workers were sympathetic and, while it was Dan who needed care around the clock, Connie was not in good health and so it made sense to all involved.

Two bedrooms became a bedroom with, first, twin beds and then at Connie's insistence a double bed, and a sitting room. A settee, two armchairs and lots of their stuff created a charming home from home, and their life continued, but now without the stress and frustration that had affected not just Connie, but Dan as well. And that's how it had been for nine months with no one knowing how ill Connie really was. Inwardly Connie probably did, but she didn't want to admit it. Not because she was scared to learn the worst, for that simply was not Connie. No, it was because she couldn't face up to what she could not resolve. She knew Dan would be distraught without her and wouldn't be able to cope. But then, one afternoon she collapsed and was rushed into hospital. To Dan, Connie had simply vanished. Where, why, he had no way of knowing. He was falling apart.

The care staff didn't know what to do. Occupation and activity to distract Dan from thinking about Connie was recommended. How about talking to him about his wife?

In their own right these were not bad ideas, they were just inadequate. Dan was yearning for his wife, preoccupied with the fact she was 'gone'. What could be so absorbing that he might 'forget' his need to find her, his longing to be with her? Television, a puzzle, a stroll in the garden? Unlikely. As for talking about Connie, this simply triggered upset, calling out and more searching. What to do? This was the question that dominated the minds of the carers and the home manager.

Imagine their relief when after nine days Connie returned from hospital and their despair when they heard what the future held. Connie only had weeks to live, maybe six, no more than 12. Just three months at most. The cancer which had been diagnosed was advanced and any treatment would be a futile gesture. For weeks she had been grimacing and complaining of pain. But no, she refused to see the doctor. There was always a reason, and there was always Dan. In her heart of hearts, Connie had always thought it might end this way. Dan had aged well. Blessed with good genes, he remained an impressive man well into his seventies, but as he was undermined by dementia his reliance on Connie came to the fore. Long before she had become physically exhausted caring for a man who towered over her, Connie had been at her wits' end, torturing herself with the question, "If anything happened to me what would happen to Dan?"

Connie had returned, but with only weeks to live. What were the staff going to do? It was at this point that I was asked to visit. I met with the care team and they talked of their worries, their concern for Dan. He hadn't done well at all while his wife had been in hospital. He wouldn't settle, his appetite had been poor, his sleep had been disturbed and for the first time some staff had started to refer to Dan as 'aggressive'. "How are we going to cope once Connie passes away?" the team leader asked. "Nine days was bad enough for Dan, but this will be, well forever." The others nodded. I explained whether it was nine minutes, nine hours or nine days the duration did not matter. Dan had dropped out of the passage of time (Stokes 2010). For Dan, unable to remember for more than moments, time did not pass. In essence he lived in the present. This meant that at any one moment in time if Connie was absent then 'life' bore unspeakable fears for him because for Dan (as with Spencer in chapter 11) his life now approximated to little more than the 'here and now'.

The staff at the home wanted to care well for Dan. They wanted to be person centred in all they did. Their knowledge of Connie and Dan, the 'home' they had helped them to create, and the relationship they had with their sons were all testimony to their commitment. But recent pressures had been so great they had asked the wrong question. So wrapped up with the stress and strain of caring for Dan, they had lost sight of what it means to be truly person centred. "How are we going to cope?" was not the question to be asked. The question that had to be grappled with was: "How is Dan going to cope?" It was not the care home that needed to be prepared for the worst, it was Dan.

His carers had become preoccupied with Dan's dementia and it was this that dominated their thinking. And because they were only relating to his dementia, all they saw was difference. But Dan was not different. Yes, he had dementia, but that could not be used to deny his love, affection and need for his wife. In essence dementia was a redundant, albeit observable fact. This was about dying, grief and bereavement. How were Dan's carers going to help a man who was about to be devastated by the loss of his wife? A man who would need to be comforted and held, both physically and emotionally.

Given the vast majority of people with dementia are over 75 years old, and care home residents are typically in their early 80s, it has always surprised me that so many care staff are unaware of the needs of people who are approaching the end of their lives. All too soon they are also shamefully prepared to abandon partners and children to their grief. In this care home no one had been trained in end-of-life care, but now we were going to meet the issue head-on.

Connie was to be helped to face her own death. Able to anticipate her end of life, she was encouraged to think about what she wanted, and how her final days should be. Doing things right meant telling her that Dan would be cared for and consoled. While nothing would make it right, was there anything that Connie knew that would help to soften what was going to be a devastating loss? Connie was typically stoical but was clearly affected by our wish to share the burden of 'what to do about Dan', but in truth there were no wonderful suggestions. My feeling was that after Connie's death Dan would face an indeterminable time of inconsolable loss not predicated on the knowledge of Connie's death but founded on her continuing absence.

As for Dan, I decided it was right to involve him in his wife's final weeks. The truth would be told not by us but by Connie. The following morning, too weak to stand, let alone walk, Connie beckoned Dan over. Sitting on the bed by his wife whose poor health could no longer be disguised Connie told him she was dying. "It's cancer, Dan. There's nothing more they can do, love. Not the doctors, nor you." And a whimsical smile crossed her lips. Her words were few, the message simple and Dan understood. And his response was a surprise to us all. Yes, disbelief and upset, but also tenderness and compassion. All acted and felt in the moment. And then it was as if no words had been exchanged. Dan remembered nothing.

However, as days passed, strangely, unexpectedly Dan seemed to know his and Connie's life was changing. While he couldn't say as much, everyone felt that his wife's illness, frailty and imminent death appeared to have affected him. Could it be that the intensity of the experience had laid down a rich emotional memory that persisted in some form or other despite the ravages of Alzheimer's disease?

Dan's manner was different – quieter, more reflective, even when apart from Connie. Yet in reality Dan rarely strayed from Connie's side. Spells away were brief and occasional, for hour after hour, day and night Dan would be with Connie. Sitting with her, lying next to her, stroking her hair, holding her hand and rubbing her back were all part of his loving repertoire, as was repeating fragments of words and disjointed sentences over and over again in a tone of voice that was soft and gentle. While unfailingly concerned and caring, staff had to be watchful in case he did something unwittingly reckless, for as Connie had once said her husband was now a big child without a shred of common sense. Watchful yes, but not rejecting, for they saw how much Dan needed to care for Connie. So at times they would ask for his help, and if the requests were simple Dan would readily respond and he would moisten Connie's lips, wipe her face and straighten her bedding.

In conversation staff would talk to Dan about Connie, about their marriage, their boys and how ill she was. Their sons all but moved into the home which was a support for Dan as he could sit quietly in their midst gazing at his wife.

Nothing was hidden from Dan. All was explained or commented upon. There was obviously a lot he couldn't comprehend, and of course nothing was remembered but always there was the all-consuming sense that Dan knew at the level of feeling what was unfolding. Dan did not fall apart as some staff had expected, while others who thought he would be immune to what was happening because of his impoverished memory were astounded by what Dan seemed able to appreciate.

Weeks passed until one early afternoon Connie slipped away. Dan, as was now his custom, had been sitting by the bed, his sons looking on. There was no trauma. No evident distress. Dan's sons were relieved that Connie's death had been peaceful. Dan held Connie's hand uttering nothing. Was there a tear? Possibly. In a world of his own who knows what he was recalling, thinking, or even truly feeling. Was the concept of death beyond him? Who can say?

Over a quarter of an hour passed. Dan sat saying

nothing, doing nothing. No one knew what to say to him. How was he to be coaxed from the bedroom? How would Dan now be? The first question was resolved by the arrival of his grandchildren. Out he went to greet them. There were smiles and hugs. But it wasn't long before the pull to be reunited with Connie proved too strong and up he got with no knowledge of the grief he was soon to endure.

Greg took him to one side and calmly said, "Mum has passed away, Dad." His reaction revealed the presence of an emotional memory for he was neither incredulous, nor did he insist that it could not be so. Instead his expression was mournful, his manner despondent. And that was the measure of the man over the coming days. Dan would sit for long periods in his sitting room seemingly staring into space. A pained expression would sometimes cross his face. But in the main he was subdued showing little interest in the world around him, and critically not once did he call out or search for Connie. I advised the family and carers not to enquire or ask questions, nor reminisce about Connie. I had a sense that in some way Dan was processing his loss and while there is a great temptation to help someone who is grieving by trying to find solutions invariably there are none. What is best is just being there, tolerating silences and accepting that you cannot make them feel better. Don, Greg and their respective wives would visit and be Dan's silent companions. Similarly staff would sit with him, some when their shift was over, while some even popped in on their days off.

Connie's funeral came and went, in truth passing Dan by. He was there in person, but not in spirit. His therapeutic journey was coming to an end. Dan had been helped to negotiate the awfulness of his wife dying and having been immersed in his wife's final weeks this stood him in good stead in the days that followed Connie's death but Dan's dementia was now to conspire against us and Dan's welfare.

The day after the funeral staff started the process of tidying Connie's belongings away. Some possessions were to be returned to her family, some little treasures to remain as keepsakes for Dan but most to be discarded. He was as involved with the dismantling of his and Connie's life together in the care home as he had been in his wife's passing. On one occasion while helping to pack things away he passed a piece of jewellery to Don and abruptly said "you look… look. No, no, not after... after". And this was possibly the last time anyone thought Dan connected with what was going on around him. Times were changing. And they would do so rapidly.

Within a week I had to advise staff to stop chatting to Dan about Connie for reminiscing was no longer giving him comfort. Instead he would look fretful and perplexed. And then one night in the early hours the searching and calling out for Connie started once more. Was it the erosion of the emotional memory trace that triggered Dan's distress, or was it the trauma of seeing their sitting room transformed into the bland anonymity of a bedroom awaiting the arrival of a new resident that was responsible for his agitation? One can only imagine the emptiness Dan encountered as his home contracted to a single room and Connie to all intents and purposes had disappeared. A departure that for Dan was unfathomable.

Tormented, longing for his wife, Dan was resistant to all efforts to calm him. Only fitful sleep brought him any respite and so it was unsurprising that his health slowly began to fail.

There was to be no happy ending. Dan's final months were sad and at times distressing to observe. Nobody could bring him peace of mind. As his grasp on reality ebbed away, his family meant less and less to him. To his sons he would shout out, "Why did you call me Dad? What's going on here?" To the rest he would bellow, "I don't know you. What are you doing here?" To them it seemed he remembered nothing at all. But that was not so. He never forgot the person to whom he was enthralled. "Where's Connie?" was his constant refrain.

Seven months after Connie died so did Dan. Of a broken heart, you could say, for his heart failed while lying on his bed, having spent an age that day pacing and calling out. But Connie was never coming back, and for Dan that was a fate he could not bear. Yet for a period of weeks around the time of Connie's death Dan and his cherished sweetheart were connected in an intimate and loving way that not even dementia could put an end to.

SIXTEEN

A step too far

Maria was born in Madrid in 1932. Her father was a chef who had yet again lost his job. Unemployable in the eyes of some, victimised in the eyes of others, Ramon made a decision. The Second World War was at an end and he decided England was where his future lay, a country where dreams could come to pass. And he had dreams. He had some money remaining from a small legacy and in his heart he knew what London needed, an authentic Spanish eating place. With little discussion, for his mind was made up, Ramon and his wife and three children packed their possessions and left for pastures new. Which is how Maria, aged 14, found herself living in Norwich!

They had arrived in London and Ramon did try, but he couldn't find employment let alone an opportunity to start his own business. So like Dick Whittington before him and incalculable numbers of others, Ramon found his vision of London as a city of plenty with streets paved with gold to be a falsehood. So more through desperation than choice, Ramon tempered his ambitions and settled his family in a city that none of them had heard of.

Life was not easy for Maria or her two younger brothers. They spoke no English and at school they were regarded as aliens as if from another world. Their welcome was less than hospitable: instead intolerance and abuse were daily occurrences.

Maria spent one year at school, and then, having reached school leaving age, she left to work in her father's small restaurant. Ramon was not frightened of hard work. In many ways he was driven to better himself. He too ran the same gamut of insults and slurs as his children and he was determined to show those who viewed him as little more than a common foreigner that they were wrong. As importantly, he needed to prove to sceptics in his own family back home that he could be a success. And he only knew two ways of doing this: work all the hours humanly possible and rule his family with a rod of iron. He was a disciplinarian who demanded respect and the more others ridiculed him the more he demanded that his family respected him. On occasions he was capable of compassion and warmth, but not only were these times few and far between you could not escape the feeling that at any moment he might explode with fury and indignation. And when he did, and having stormed out of the room as was his wont, Maria's mother would comfort her children by saying, "Don't be afraid. It's just words. He takes after his father." But their grandfather's story was a more tragic matter, as we shall learn.

Like her mother and brothers, Maria was cowed and

intimidated by Ramon. Not because she suffered at his hands, for while he would angrily gesture and threaten he never struck out, yet his actions were abusive nevertheless. Always having to be subservient, walking on eggshells for fear of upsetting him, constantly censoring her words, denying her own desires, isolated and trapped in a life she didn't want. Yes, she was abused.

Maria and her mother worked interminable hours, waiting on tables, working in the kitchen, clearing, cleaning and tidying. Without much reward, for her pay was meagre and her father was rarely forthcoming with praise. Maria aged 20 was embittered and resentful. Their father's restaurant, now in larger premises, had become a success, but at what price? Yes, they had some status and English was no longer a foreign tongue, so the family had begun to feel they belonged. As Ramon would say, their life was way better than it would have been if they had remained at home in Madrid. But did it feel better? Maria didn't think so. Her mother said little but never seemed happy, while Ramon was never satisfied. At his core was a discontent that meant life was never as he wanted it to be. As for her brothers, they flew the nest. The restaurant couldn't really support them as well, so Ramon did not protest when they took their own paths, got jobs elsewhere, found love and in both cases moved to London. They were free of their tyrannical father, and from afar they respected him. But visits home were rare. Maria felt her confinement even more.

Maria's life was monotonous and lonely. She could see no way out. Her mother needed her, her father needed her, and the restaurant needed her. Her life was mapped out. She despaired and her bitterness grew. Years passed and Maria carried the unwanted burden of a life being wasted. Her expression was sour and her manner cold. However, in March 1963 the unexpected happened. Without warning Ramon had a massive heart attack and died hours later. Shocked and saddened, but also relieved Maria was free. As was her mother. She sold the restaurant and returned to Spain to be close to her sisters. She gave Maria a small amount of money – "For now you start your life" – but sadly Maria did not prosper; instead she floundered. She didn't have the confidence to go to London to be near her brothers, but anyway they had their own lives, especially Miguel who was now married with a young family. She had no desire to return to Spain for that now felt a foreign country. Instead she rented a flat in Norwich and got a job as a restaurant manager for a while. She detested the work, but it was what she knew, and it was what she did well.

Aged 31 she had never felt more alone. Her disposition didn't help; it was a barrier not only to friendships but also probably to ever marrying for she seemed incapable of showing warmth and affection. Nearly every fibre of her being revealed she was her father's daughter, although in Maria's case rage was replaced by festering anger and self-pity. But not all marriages are made in heaven and against all the odds she did marry.

Alan dined regularly at the restaurant, always by himself. At the end of the evening he would always be the last to leave. One after-dinner drink would be followed by another, and then another. He clearly had no reason to leave; while he never said, there was obviously no one waiting for him at home. Maria didn't feel sorry for him, for compassion did not come easily to her. Rather, she understood why he'd prefer to be somewhere other than a place that only masqueraded as home. Just after midnight she would allow the staff to leave and that's how Maria came to be sitting alone with Alan, sharing a nightcap or two, for she too had nowhere to go other than what was home in name only. Loneliness brought them together, and it was rather a desire to end their lonely lives than any real attraction that resulted in them getting married. With him more than 15 years older than Maria, Alan's marriage to her was one of convenience. While this didn't prevent them from having a daughter, it stopped them from having a close and intimate relationship.

Unsurprisingly it wasn't long before Maria and Alan started to drift apart. He had an affair and Maria, who for many a year had sought comfort in drinking, started to drink heavily. She was trapped once more, this time in a loveless marriage to a man who wanted little to do with her. Once more her life was desolate and joyless but in reality this had been her life for as long as she could remember.

Alcohol was her salvation but it was also to be her downfall. She and Alan parted to live separate lives. Caught in the middle was their daughter, Beatrice. She moved between the two of them until eventually her mother's drinking became too much. Maria's outlook on life was always pessimistic but when drunk she was morose and resentful. Beatrice loved her mother but as a person even her daughter found her unappealing. Her mother's morbid and depressive outlook was dragging her down, so much so that after yet another bitter argument between her mother and father she could take it no more. She sided with Alan and went to live with her father, never to return to Maria. For Maria this was the final blow. Alone once more, her unhappy life unravelled. Still only in her early 50s she whiled away empty, pointless hours with alcohol as her sole companion. Invariably after a bout of heavy drinking Alan and Beatrice would be on the receiving end of abusive phone calls. Ranting on about the unfairness of it all and the people who were annoying her. And it wasn't only Alan and Beatrice she alienated. Her brothers and their wives also dreaded Maria's calls, and despite numerous pleas, coming to stay was never going to happen. For Maria, just as home was in name only, so was 'family'.

Within a decade Maria was living in hostels and dependent on alcohol. She tried on more than a few occasions to stop drinking but to no avail. She would abstain for a few weeks, then appreciate her life was still the same and faced with this harsh reality she would be consumed by despondency; once more she would seek solace in alcohol. A diagnosis of alcohol-related brain damage was made following an accident, when worse for wear she stepped in front of a car and was knocked down. Two years later, while drunk she fell down some steps. The hospital notes recorded 'alcohol-induced persistent dementia'. She was 65.

Women are probably more vulnerable to the neurotoxic effects of alcohol and repeated withdrawal may be associated with greater cognitive impairment. Maria's long-term excessive drinking had resulted in dementia and, while some symptoms are relatively nonprogressive in abstinent ex-drinkers, or even partially reversible (see Ralph's story, chapter 17), Maria's use of alcohol did not abate. Even though alcohol-related dementia is less progressive than Alzheimer's disease, Maria's evolving intellectual decline and physical dilapidation were placing her on an inevitable path to residential care – that is, if she survived. Chronic alcohol misuse is associated with increased mortality and Maria was a vulnerable adult. Falls, assaults and minor road traffic accidents were continuing features of her life. Nevertheless she lived to tell the tale and when eventually a decision was taken for her to enter a care home it was, at least in the beginning, the best thing that had happened to her in years.

There is only one reason why anyone should live in a care home and that is to get a better life – not measured against how life may once have been, a time from bygone years when life was characterised by family, friends, purpose and value, but life as it was prior to being admitted. A life that for many people with dementia is characterised by isolation, vulnerability and stressed relationships. Without doubt Maria's life was better. Now safe from exploitation and self-inflicted harm, cared for, and most significantly no longer able to drink, her dementia stabilised and her health improved. But of course her manner didn't. She remained who she had always been. Aggressive and abusive on arrival, detached and remote thereafter. The home manager decided to take action. Maria had been a resident for months. Every day she was angry, she would yell out profanities, at times she would cry – and not once had anyone visited. Might a visit from her daughter help lift her mother's mood?

Beatrice had rarely seen her mother in recent years so who knows what prompted her to agree to the manager's request, and then inexplicably decide to become closely involved in her mother's welfare. For years she had ignored her mother's plight, but no longer. Who knows whether it was guilt, sympathy or obligation that was motivating her, but Beatrice insisted the home do more to make her mother's final years happy. She appreciated the care Maria was being given, but what she couldn't accept was the austere life her mother was living. And it was barren. With few belongings her room was by no stretch of the imagination homely. In fact 'institutional' would best sum up her Spartan room. Bare walls, a bed which would not have looked out of place on a hospital ward, a wardrobe, armchair and vanity unit on which were placed her meagre possessions constituted her 'home'. A few paltry items she could call her own, nobody who cared enough to visit – if ever proof was needed that Maria's life had been unhappy and unfulfilling, and ultimately unforgiving, this was it. Yet at this point in time, toward the end of her mother's life, Beatrice stepped in.

While little things could be done to make her room more inviting, Beatrice argued that if her mother was invited into the social life of the home this might help lift her mood. The home had a rich diary of weekly activity and social events to choose from. So Maria was encouraged to join in the 'sing-along' group, 'Fun for all' – but not for Maria. While the others sang along to well-known songs Maria sat in their midst quiet, sullen and clearly ill at ease, eventually walking away. The arts and craft group held no interest for her and while she tolerated the morning exercise classes she never joined in. Balls passed her by, balloons were never patted back, her arms remained crossed as if she was wilfully registering a protest.

Even though it had been her suggestion Beatrice was not unduly surprised by her mother's reaction for she had rarely warmed to people and they had rarely warmed to her. "She struggled socially throughout her whole life," Beatrice told the home manager. "Not to worry," was the response. The manager asked Beatrice to tell her as much as she could about her mother's life: "We have a reminiscence group and everyone enjoys it." Sometimes the home showed old films or played archive recordings, at other times using all sorts of artefacts and memorabilia to share memories, while residents were also encouraged to bring along their own mementoes to talk about. "Everyone joins in. It's impossible not to. Your mum will also. You see, they lose themselves in their memories, and so many memories aren't affected by dementia, especially those from long ago." The words of the manager were to be prophetic.

Beatrice told her something about Maria's family history. How Maria's parents had owned a restaurant, and for years she had worked in this and other restaurants and how she had come to England when a teenager, having grown up in Madrid. Armed with this knowledge, at the next reminiscence session the activity coordinator had to hand a 'city breaks' brochure, as well as some photographs of old Madrid that she had downloaded. She informed the group that today we're going to share memories of 'where we grew up'. Maria was her normal detached self but sitting next to her the activity coordinator placed a photograph of the Plaza Mayor in her hands, and then one of the Royal Palace. Maria just stared and said nothing. "Do you recognise these places, Maria?" She didn't reply. The conversation moved on, other residents contributed, memories were triggered and stories flowed. Throughout Maria sat there distant and withdrawn.

At the next meeting with no real expectation that Maria would join in, the activity coordinator continued with the theme of childhood memories. She leant forward in her chair and pressed into Maria's hands another photograph of a Madrid landmark, this time a photo of the Retiro Park and its boating lake. Nothing! No response. No flicker of interest. But what no one could have known was that Maria was thinking. Not simply thinking but ruminating, processing what she had been shown, resurrecting memories, edging closer and closer to a catastrophic reaction.

When the group next met, just two days later, one of the residents brought a photograph and her family bible. The photo was of the elderly woman as a young child, with her brothers and sisters, mother and father, and two of her grandparents. The photo struck a chord. As the manager had told Beatrice, all joined in. All that is, except Maria. There was a babble of conversation as family days were recalled, comments were made about the clothes people wore and what children were made to wear all those years ago, and how awful it was to pose for formal family photographs. Happy banter filled the room, in stark contrast to the sight of Maria sitting silently in her chair. This should have been the time to desist, but instead it was taken as another opportunity to try to draw her into the conversation. The road to hell is paved with good intentions and this was to be no exception. A fateful question was asked. "Maria, you grew up in Spain. Did all your family come to England with you?"

Maria's screams were ear piercing. Screams that went on and on, and on. Carers came rushing into the lounge. Residents were ushered away. Attempts to accompany Maria to her room failed. She could not be consoled. Every hand that touched her was knocked away. Screams interspersed with sobs, until an exhausted Maria curled herself into a ball and sank deep into the armchair, unresponsive to all that was going on around her. And there she stayed. She slept in the chair most of that night. Just before dawn one of the night staff managed to coax her to her room where she was bathed, assisted into her night dress and tucked into bed.

Who can say what memories and feelings had surfaced to traumatise Maria? Was it her unhappy teenage years in England? Might it have been her father's abusive behaviour? Or years later having been deserted by her daughter? Or could it have been the death of her grandfather, a volatile but affectionate man who Maria had been particularly close to?

The siege of Madrid during the Spanish Civil War lasted more than two years, from the end of 1936 to March 1939, when the city finally fell to the Nationalist army of General Franco. The city held by forces loyal to the Republic was not only besieged, it was bombarded from the air. Throughout people suffered increasingly from a lack of food and warm clothes. Deprivation, death and devastation were Maria's childhood experiences, one day to become her memories. Bombs crashing just yards away, taking their daily toll of victims. Her home destroyed. The blackness of death and destruction both shocking and incomprehensible to her in equal measure.

When Madrid finally fell, revenge was sought and in the immediate aftermath tens of thousands of Republican soldiers and sympathisers were executed or died in prison. Maria's grandfather, a prominent Republican sympathiser, was dragged out of his house late one morning, taken to the local square and shot. The terror was etched on the faces of his family as they were made to watch. Standing next to her father, a terrified Maria, just seven years of age, wet herself as she saw her grandfather die. Her young life had not been a fiesta bathed in golden Spanish sunshine to be celebrated in a reminiscence group.

Whenever services, activities or products are recommended as being 'good' for people living with dementia there needs to be a period of reflection, for 'dementia care' does not exist. Instead we must accept that we care for people with dementia, each of whom is unique, at a different point on their journey, and resourced differently to cope with what lies before them. Interventions can never be 'one size fits all'. We need to ask who may benefit, at what stage of intellectual decline, in what settings, and for how long until a regard for the person says now is the time to stop and review what is being done. People with severe dementia do not benefit from cognitive stimulation therapy (Spector *et al* 2011);

new technology is not supportive of people with marked dementia if they have to engage with the adaptations; some people with dementia are distressed by familiar activities because they know or simply sense they cannot perform as well as they once did; and not all like to look back and reminisce because their life story was never a source of happiness and comfort. Maria was such a person. Paradoxically the very efforts taken to lift Maria's mood led to her once more enduring the darkest days of depression. They should have left her be, for person-centred care is about knowing the individual and allowing them to be who they are and who they have always been. Even if that means they never know joy.

SEVENTEEN

When two leopards meet

The care home manager feared that at the very least he would be suspended. The police were in the building. The safeguarding team had been informed and a senior practitioner would be arriving shortly. And then there were the families, neither closely involved with their aged parents but they had nevertheless been told. Ralph had a son and while his father had only been in the home a few weeks no one could recall him ringing to find out how his father was settling in let alone visiting. A message had been left asking him to call. Judy's two daughters were occasional visitors and neither was close to their mother. It wasn't just the infrequency and brevity of their visits that told you this was not a loving family, it was more their awkward body language, barren conversation and far-away looks that betrayed their desire to be elsewhere.

Judy had lived in the home for several months and she was a character. Diagnosed with vascular dementia she had gradually succumbed to the ravages of a disease that mercilessly eroded her self-awareness and intellectual abilities. She descended from being at first eccentric to becoming a vulnerable and pitiful caricature of the woman she had once been. A glamorous woman, vain and self-absorbed. Yet while she now struggled to remember and reason, the essence of who she was remained. In the care home getting Judy ready for the day was never as simple as a wash and brush of her hair. That would never be enough. To Judy her makeup was not a luxury but a necessity. "My dear, I'm not leaving here without my face on," she said, and nor would she. Every morning it was the same. Wash, dress and then an inordinate amount of time spent doing Judy's hair and make-up. And despite her years she could still look quite stunning. "It's bone structure, darling. It never leaves you. Unlike the men in your life," she said, her words dissolving into a throaty laugh.

Her life was now better than the one she had been living, if for no other reason than she no longer faced daily ridicule at having become a 'painted lady'. Falling prey to the 'half inch' that trips up many people with dementia as their abilities and judgement are undermined Judy's eyeliner was put on just too thick, her lipstick was invariably smudged, while rouge transformed her cheekbones into jutting peaks of shocking crimson. But no more. Judith was once more the woman she needed to be. And this didn't stop with her once more being glamorous. Judith adored men, especially younger men. She was flirtatious. She would follow male carers around, lean seductively in the office doorway whenever the handsome home manager visited the unit and would hover around any good-looking young relative whose path she happened to cross. Yes, Judith needed the company of men. While some were offended by what they saw as her disinhibited ways, most saw her as simply having harmless fun. As for Judith I doubt whether she had much awareness into how she appeared to others. Yet even if she had I don't think she would have cared.

He was not young but at 71 Ralph was once more an attractive man. He had arrived at the home a few days previously. Alcohol-related dementia had resulted in his life becoming more and more chaotic. Friendless, no one had known about his dilapidated life although many knew about the mindless ranting of a dishevelled man who was often the worse for wear having drunk too much. He lived alone in a flat with his life insidiously falling apart around him. Bills unpaid, food rotting in the fridge, crockery and cutlery unwashed for weeks, soiled bed linen, grime and grubbiness all around testified to this man's inadequacy. And then he fell in the street. Was he drunk? Possibly. Had he been drinking? Definitely.

Taken to hospital barely conscious, he was found to have broken his right arm, dislocated his left shoulder and broken two ribs. One month in hospital turned into two while he not only healed but social services attempted to extricate him from his squalid home life. The doctors were adamant that he was unlikely to comply with his medication regime, while his physiotherapist was equally sure he wouldn't cooperate with rehabilitation. All knew he would resort to drinking again. His need for a care home was the unanimous call. And Ralph agreed. Two months in hospital had worked near wonders. No alcohol, a good diet and the medical treatment he needed had restored Ralph to a relative picture of good health. With a degree of insight restored he left behind his previous life not knowing he was soon to be bewitched, bothered and, if not bewildered, then besotted with a woman who was to find herself equally smitten.

The personal information that accompanied Ralph to his new home was meagre. His condition was known, as were the details of his recent chaotic lifestyle but all else was sketchy. He had returned to England about seven years previously having lived in southern Africa for more than 40 years, where he'd worked as a mining engineer. Subsequently we learnt he had been one of the best. Resourceful and ingenious, Ralph had not only been skilled at identifying new ore deposits but he was often called in when specialist mining equipment was needed to improve safety or increase productivity. Africa had got into his blood and he often said he would never return home. Zambia, Zimbabwe, Tanzania and South Africa were where his heart belonged. He adored the climate and outdoor life. He worked hard, lived hard and invariably gained notoriety wherever he put his roots down for his heavy drinking and quick temper. A temper that bordered on rage when faced with a personal slight, the inadequacies of others or when he simply felt the world was turning against him. A despairing state of mind that would thrive whenever he drank too much. He married but he had been divorced for years, his wife returning to England with their son, Kevin when the little boy was only four years old. Thereafter the sum total of his contact with his son had been the occasional letter, birthday cards that invariably arrived days, sometimes weeks late, and even rarer visits that nearly always ended acrimoniously.

Judy was immediately drawn to Ralph who, despite the ravages inflicted by his heavy drinking, had profited from his life in Africa. Swarthy, rugged and now restored to health the chemistry between them was obvious to all. Judy would saunter up to Ralph with the devil in her eyes, and he responded with relish. Yet this was not a blossoming relationship founded on tenderness and companionship. This was raw sexual attraction. They would walk off with each other and be found in bedrooms or quiet corners fondling and kissing. Some staff were amused that an aged couple were able to rekindle such depths of fervent passion, but in the main most talked of dementia and disinhibition. Both Judy's and Ralph's care plans described the need for staff to be watchful, to preserve the self-respect and dignity of both by keeping them apart, and the need to distract them with activities. But these were two determined people, well able to seek each other out and realistically what activity could anyone suggest that would be more compelling than the sexual attraction they had for each other?

Unsurprisingly, staff within the home were under increasing strain. As relatives and visitors commented and complained, and the home manager became more strident in his instructions to "Keep them away from each other", all feared the repercussions if a line was crossed. And what was that line? When Ralph and Judy were discovered having sexual intercourse.

In the early hours one morning they were discovered

in Judy's room. Not a chance discovery, for Ralph had woken and had decided to seek out Judy but the combination of his fragile recall and the anonymity of the bedroom doors distinguished by inconsequential room numbers and name plates that mean little to any of the residents living with dementia conspired against him finding her with ease. So he walked in and out of several rooms disturbing and possibly frightening others. The commotion attracted staff and that's how they discovered him as he lay alongside Judy. Ralph's temper got the better of him. He shouted, cursed and resisted all attempts to extricate him from Judy's bed. Judy was screaming, "Leave my man alone." And as further testimony to her confusion, "Get out of my house." Nobody knew what to do. The nurse in charge talked of calling the GP, or maybe having to call the police. As minutes passed who knows whether it was exhaustion or exasperation that eventually overtook all else. With lights on, the door open and a gaggle of nurses and carers looking down on them, desire and passion must have evaporated. Ralph, despairing, got out of the bed and muttering to himself walked out of the room paying little heed to the staff as he brushed past them.

This was never to be allowed to happen again. A team meeting that afternoon came up with a solution. Part way down one of the bedroom corridors where the extension started there was a swing door and this would now be 'baffled' with two handles that would have to be pulled in opposite directions to open it. During the day the door would remain open but at night it would be closed and Ralph would be moved to a room on the other side of what would now be an insurmountable barrier. A revised care plan informed night staff that as they walked the hallways they must ensure they made regular and frequent visits to the 'baffled' area in case any residents had walked out of their rooms and found themselves confined.

Two nights after Ralph moved to his new room an almighty noise reverberated around the unit. The sound of wood splintering and a door violently swinging back against a wall. The trouble was so much else was going on. It was just unfortunate timing. A resident had soiled her bed and was being changed and comforted. Another resident, lost and confused, was being accompanied by a nurse back to her room. Meanwhile the nurse-in-charge had been called to another unit as the doctor had arrived and she was requesting an emergency hospital admission for an elderly gentleman who had suffered a stroke.

At this ill-fated time, Ralph commenced his quest to find Judy. Leaving his room, within a few strides he encountered the baffled door. No one knows how many times he must have pulled at the handles or pushed and pulled at the door before his actions became more extreme. Equally nobody could say why he wasn't dissuaded from seeking Judy, having encountered the baffled door, but he wasn't. Was the motivation unrestrained sexual desire, defiance or as the psychiatrist wrote later that day, 'disinhibited violent impulses the consequence of dementia, probably frontal pathology'. All possible explanations but true understanding would have to wait for another day.

Ralph kicked the door over and over again with such ferocity the lock came away and the door flew back crashing against the wall. The noise resounded down the hallway but there was no one to investigate. Many minutes later one of the nurses arrived at the scene and immediately thought there had been a break-in. Scared at the thought intruders were in the building she telephoned the manager who told her to call the police and he would be at the home within the hour. When he arrived the police were already there. There were no trespassers in the home, or in the grounds. In fact there was no evidence of a break-in. The only damage was to the internal door. And they already knew who the miscreant was. Not through powers of deduction but as they searched the building they had walked into Judy's room and discovered her and Ralph having sex. The line had been crossed in dramatic fashion. And if this was not bad enough, Judy had a head wound. A minor one, but an injury nevertheless. Had Ralph assaulted her? Was this rape?

The doctor who had been called back to the home examined Judy and said there were no defensive injuries nor any bruising associated with forced intercourse. She felt the head wound was too minor to have dazed Judy and said if she had banged her head against the headboard possibly during a moment of unbridled excitement this would have been the type of cut and bruising she would have expected.

Other than damage to property the police were satisfied no other crime had been committed and there was no way Ralph was going to be charged. Yet what could not be dismissed was the fact that those with a duty of care had failed two vulnerable adults with dementia, both of whom had sustained minor injuries and had engaged in sexual intercourse when neither had the intellectual capacity to give informed consent. But was this really so?

I was asked to assess both Judy and Ralph to establish whether they had mental capacity for the decision in question. It went without saying that Ralph's actions were unwise. In addition, the couple had engaged in an act that had caused the home manager and his staff worry if not offence, and probably was going to mortify both Judy and Ralph's children. However, these were not grounds to say they were incapable of making an informed decision.

In outline, if not in great detail, both Judy and Ralph could remember and communicate what they had done, even though Ralph did not believe the doors had been 'locked'. He said they were jammed, but he could remember kicking the door "Bloody hard!". However, when we talked about the consequences of their decision to have intercourse, the effect this might have on others and even on their own futures, it was clear that neither of them had anything other than a scant understanding of how their actions would be perceived and nor did they grasp any consequences there might be for them other than the literal one of having enjoyed sex together. It was also evident that Judy's understanding of her relationship with Ralph did not correspond with reality. She consistently talked about him being "her man" and how they had known each other for some time, enjoying many a romantic assignation. Consequently my opinion was that neither Judy nor Ralph had the mental capacity to make an informed decision to have sexual intercourse at the time it needed to be made. But could we support the decisions they had taken because it was in their 'best interest'?

At face value the answer was no. They were not in a stable relationship, and even though there was no evidence of resistance on Judy's part, could it be said she would have engaged in casual sex with a man she had recently met and knew nothing about had her judgement not have been compromised by her dementia? This was reinforced by the way she spoke about Ralph and her view that they were romantic lovers. Similarly would Ralph have acted in the way he had if his brain had not been damaged by years of alcohol abuse? Common sense and morality suggested not. Clearly something had to be done to protect and promote the welfare of both, but what?

Three weeks had passed since the events of that night and Ralph and Judy were walking out of her room late one afternoon. He had his arm round her and as they walked down the hallway into the lounge they passed the home manager who smiled. Judy gave him one of her inviting looks and Ralph winked, and all knew what had transpired. Ralph and Judy had again had a romantic assignation or, more accurately, an hour or so of mutual sexual gratification. And all was well.

Two weeks earlier, at the urgently convened professionals and family meeting, Judy's youngest daughter could not have been clearer: "But that's mum. I don't know what all the fuss is about. I'm sure my sister would say the same." And she did. Judy had always been promiscuous. Not only had she been married three times – the sisters were half-sisters – she had had numerous affairs, and being a chorus girl and then a bit-part actress she always had plenty of opportunity to indulge in her passion for men. Infatuation, reckless behaviour and then regret was the pattern of her life. "Never again," she would say, but any willpower she might have would dissipate as soon as the next attractive man showed her any attention and once more she found herself in love. And for Judy her sexual feelings were often embellished with romantic fantasies for these nourished her need to be loved, not just desired. Her behaviour was typical and her relationship with Ralph unremarkable. He was simply another in a lengthy line of male conquests. Judy was acting as all who knew her would have predicted.

As for Ralph: "Mum left Dad because of his affairs. I don't how many, I don't really care. He abandoned us... Mum always said he was a womaniser. And he didn't care who he hurt. If he wanted something, and you didn't give it to him, you had no chance. He was off. And you didn't cross Dad. You didn't stand in his way for, if you did, you'd regret it. And I expect he's still the same today. Leopards don't change their spots, do they?"

Maybe he was no longer a womaniser but Ralph still had an eye for a woman, and unquestionably he had shown you still didn't get in his way if he wanted something, or somebody! He was working in Tanzania in the mid-1960s when the government nationalised its gold mines. Nothing was the same, opportunities disappeared and Ralph moved to Zambia, started working in the copper mines and two years later the government did the same. All prospecting and mining licences reverted to the state. Ralph had done well in his two years in Zambia. He had earned a lot, gambled and won, and had bought a fine house that was now requisitioned by the state. At a knock-down price it was to be the home of a senior government official. Consumed by a sense of injustice, rage got the better of him and rather than see this happen, even though it meant losing everything and gaining nothing other than perverse satisfaction Ralph blew the house up! Compared to this, a baffled internal door was nothing.

Person-centred care is not about letting people be who we wish them to be, it means accepting who they are. And sometimes that means difficult decisions have to be made. Decisions that challenge how we think people should be, how they should behave and even what is right or wrong, good or bad. Ralph and Judy were two unconventional, you could say unappealing, people but that is who they were. None of their children were surprised or offended by what had happened. "Mum is Mum. Can't you leave them be. She's having fun. Would you rather she was miserable?"

And who has the right to say it should be any other way? Should we not say it's okay to be you, and only if your actions cause harm do we reflect on whether it is 'wrong' to be you? Ralph and Judy were causing no harm. As a couple they had found gratification, intimacy and pleasure in each other's company, and I suspect in Judy's heart she had also found love, and this time her man was going nowhere.

EIGHTEEN

Both sides now

Already nearly six o'clock and it had been a dreary, tedious journey. Late November, mists hovered, the sky was various shades of grey, and fine rain had fallen throughout my two-hour drive. A dull day seamlessly became dark as evening drew in early. To the miserable weather was added countless other vehicles, headlights shimmering in the misty drizzle, all creeping at snail's pace. And I was late, much later than I'd expected to be.

Unsurprisingly, I was relieved to have arrived eventually at the care home. But little was I to know that my relief would dissolve within minutes. As I entered the nicely-appointed, hotel-style reception my heart sank. There was no warmth, no cheerfulness, no comfortable feel. It was lifeless, soulless, but not peaceful. And that was why I had travelled all this way. As I approached the reception desk I heard Frances' yells and shrieks emanating from deep within the building. Whether you were living, working or visiting, her noisy behaviour disturbed everyone, for no one was immune to her intrusive screeching.

Suzie, the new home manager who had only taken up her appointment a couple of weeks previously, had asked if I could offer some advice because: "My staff are at their wits' end. I know it's because Frances has dementia so I'm not expecting miracles but any advice will be welcome."

I wasn't going to work miracles but I was going to offer hope as it was highly improbable that the reason for Frances' unintelligible shouting was because she had dementia. As I have said on many occasions, what people with dementia share in common (such as memory loss and language problems) you can attribute to their brain disease. But what they do not share, for example incessant screaming, can rarely be attributed to their dementia. "Are you sure?" asked Suzie. "I mean her dementia is really bad. And she can't be reacting to anything because she's unaware of what's going on around her. Don't forget she's completely blind too."

Yes, Frances wasn't simply living with dementia, she was also frail and had total sight loss. However, while relating to the outside world would be difficult, being 'no longer inside herself' was another matter. David Baddiel, writing about his dad's dementia, talks about "present absence sitting among the ruins" as "his face, I think, is turning to the wall". People who are no longer inside themselves. I understand when partners and children say 'they've gone' or 'that's not my mum'; when all that was known appears to have departed and the person acts in ways they've never done before, especially if that behaviour is heartless, offensive or antisocial. However, more often than not the meaningless is meaningful, while what appears out of character can be the efforts of people with dementia to communicate who they are and what they need. Their words and actions are affected, distorted and rendered mysterious by their diminished, dismantled capacity to think, remember and talk.

We walked down the hallway into the lounge. Frances had fallen quiet. We came across one of the nurses and, as we were talking, Frances started again. Looking at Suzie, the nurse said, "This can't go on. She's upsetting everybody."

Genuinely curious I asked, "Why do you think she's doing it?"

Her look was incredulous. "Haven't you been told? She's got dementia. Severe dementia."

"Yes, but Frances is living with dementia all the time, yet she doesn't scream all the time. It might feel that she does, but she doesn't. So might there be something else going on?"

"Like what? Nothing happens. She just starts."

"And when she does, what do you do?"

"Most of the time we leave her be. Hoping she'll stop before she sets any of the others off. Because that's what happens."

All three of us walked to Frances' room, arriving just as two carers were about to transfer her from an armchair to her bed using a hoist. She was quiet. As she was lifted once more her yells reverberated around the building. Standing not six feet away, from within her small frame were coming the mightiest screams and you could understand why the nurse had said something needed to be done. And something could be done: as Frances, severely demented and blind was effortlessly elevated in the hoist – "Here we go, Frances" – I'd noticed her hands that had been resting on her lap had, as if a trap had been sprung, become tightly clenched fists. Turning to Suzie, I said: "It's not her dementia. She's frightened."

Why hadn't her fear reaction been noticed before? Why hadn't any of her carers considered the possibility that she was distressed? It was because they hadn't looked, they hadn't wondered, because they already knew. It was because she had dementia. The home didn't care for people; it warehoused the consequences of dementia. People were viewed as grotesque remnants of who they once were, their fragments of behaviour invariably understood as mere symptoms of disease.

Sitting in a world of darkness, faced with unexpected noise and mystifying approaches, was it that surprising Frances would be frightened? And her distress could not be eased by her knowing that nothing bad had ever happened for the severity of her dementia meant all she experienced would have been effaced within moments. To Frances (as with Spencer, chapter 11, and Dan, chapter 15), only the immediacy of her present existed. There was no before. She had lost her place in time to the point there was only 'now', and if she was frightened then fear was all that made up her life.

And what was the response of Frances' carers to her feelings of fear? To abandon her to her isolation and horrors. No wonder her cries persisted.

Suzie was aghast but also inspired. She wanted to

know more. Her background was in mental health services so the world of emotions, disturbed behaviour and poor adjustment was not new to her. She had a particular interest in depression. Now she appreciated there was more going on than met the eye and realised her job was much more than managing staff rotas and ensuring the physical welfare of her residents. In a matter of weeks Suzie had changed how she, and critically her staff team, responded to the behaviours of those she cared for. First was Frances. Whenever she was screaming someone was to sit with her, hold her hand and soothe her with comforting words. During care tasks or as Frances was approached there was now to be a reassuring commentary. It wasn't that she could understand but she would now be aware of a kindly presence. The frequency and length of her screaming episodes were reduced by over 60 per cent.

The next was Peter who had been labelled as unpredictably bad-tempered and aggressive. He was, until his actions were seen as the result of pain, and Suzie arranged for him to have a dental appointment. If I remember correctly, he had a couple of fillings and five teeth removed! Now free of pain, while never a saint thereafter, his behaviour improved beyond all recognition.

Emily was little trouble but her circular hand movements were seen as bizarre. She seemed to have little emotional investment in her actions. It was just what she did while walking, or while sitting quietly. Sometimes she would lean over a table or face a wall and perform the action. Disconcertingly she would on occasions do it while standing in front of somebody. Intimidating, yes, but she frightened no one for she was never threatening. Rather, she was always composed, and often her actions were accompanied by a serene smile. Suzie was curious. She asked her sister what she thought Emily might be doing, and although she didn't know and it had never crossed her mind to think why, now she'd been asked she thought it might be to do with Emily's work. She had been employed for years in the textile industry. Her job had been to feel the cloth and if she felt a snag she would pull it through. It was a comfortable behaviour from long ago that today provided occupation and possibly even reassurance. Suzie made a decision. Around the home, pieces of cloth appeared – cloth Emily would contentedly run her hands over time and time again as she lost herself once more in what to her was a meaningful action.

Finding out as much as she could about her residents became a passion for Suzie. She decided that from now on all her residents would have their life stories written down. All would be seen as individuals, and who they are would come first in order to ensure their lives would be in keeping with the way they might like things done and how they might want things to be.

Robert walked the hallways. That wouldn't have been a problem except where one of the hallways dog-legged. Rather than turning abruptly right, Robert would repeatedly walk through the door that faced him, into the room of a frail elderly woman with advanced dementia. Sometimes he would stand looking at Heather as she sat in her armchair, at other times he would move some of her things around, but nothing was ever damaged. She was too withdrawn to respond so nobody knew whether

Robert's presence upset her or not, but one day, as in his mind he was probably rearranging her cushions, he was seen holding one over her face. An inadvertent act, but the knee-jerk reaction was panic. The first suggestion was to lock Heather's room to keep Robert out. However, to Suzie this meant locking Heather in and she was not prepared to have one of her most vulnerable residents behind a locked door. So if Heather could not be protected then Robert had to be stopped and the conversation soon drifted to her GP being asked to prescribe antipsychotic medication. I advised Suzie that in most instances the risks outweighed the benefits, and in essence the only reason the medication would be prescribed would be to sedate Robert thereby ensuring he spent most of the day in his chair passive and drowsy. "But we do need to do something," said Suzie and she was right. But that something shouldn't be at the cost of limiting Robert's movements through the use of sedation.

Sometimes simple changes to a care home environment can reduce the likelihood of somebody entering a room or trying to leave the building. Doors we don't want residents to take notice of can be designed out by being the same colour as the adjacent walls. A further way to disguise doors is to run the corridor handrail across the door. A person with dementia is likely to perceive the handrail as continuous rather than seeing it for what it is, namely a handrail fragment placed on the door. Fire exits with a window pane can be disguised with the introduction of a sill and painting the door the colour of the adjacent wall to become a window to look through rather than a frustrating locked door. However, my design idea was to place four horizontal strips of sticky black tape on the floor outside Heather's door. Many people with dementia have visuoperceptual difficulties and it is known that patterned flooring can be misperceived, and in the absence of reasoning they can truly misinterpret a shadow on the floor for a hole in the floor. What resembled a cattle-grid might to Robert be a real obstacle or hazard to be avoided. And so it proved. On reaching the door to Heather's room he saw the 'grid', he would pause and on a few occasions he would try to step highly over the first strip before stepping back. However, most times without more ado he would veer right and carry on his way. Heather was undisturbed and Robert's quality of life was equally unaffected. Not long after Suzie was similarly creative.

Jenny caused all sorts of chaos as she walked in and out of residents' rooms emptying their drawers of clothes. But she didn't confine her attention to the bedrooms she passed. As she found her way around the care home, more by chance than intent, she would come across coats, jackets and cardigans in the office, the lounge, anywhere where people might temporarily lay their clothes to rest. The servery and linen trolley also provided rich pickings. Tea towels, sheets, pillow cases would all disappear, and that was the problem. Once removed, the challenge was recovering them, for Jenny would not so much hide them as put them away in both obvious and obscure places. And even the obvious places were a cause for concern, as Jenny would go into any resident's room and place another resident's garments in their drawers, after which perplexed staff would desperately try to remember what belonged to whom. That is until their relatives appeared and then it was as much dealing with their anger as it was returning items to their rightful owners. Jenny was not being malicious. She was disoriented and muddled and having gathered as much as she could carry she would put things away, and where that might be was governed by proximity and what she saw as a suitable storage place – and that didn't necessarily mean a drawer or wardrobe.

Having learnt from how we responded to the actions of Robert there was no talk of restricting Jenny's movements, locking doors or prescribing antipsychotic medication. Instead Suzie purchased six wash baskets and eight brightly coloured storage boxes. They were placed in each bedroom hallway, in the lounge and outside the office. At the start of the day the wash baskets were filled with the unwanted clothes and bed linen Suzie had asked her staff to bring in. So prominent and enticing were the baskets it was less effort and more alluring for Jenny to empty the baskets than it was for her to walk in and out of rooms opening drawers and cupboards. Similarly the cheerfully coloured storage boxes were handy for Jenny to tidy away the clothes and bedding she'd collected because that is what she was doing for that's what she had done for decades. First as a chamber maid in the best seafront hotel in the town and then as a housekeeper in the care home where she now lived! Creativity and a respect for Jenny's life history had led Suzie to a solution that is known as *functional displacement*, an intervention I had used on several occasions (Stokes 2008). Functional displacement provides a person with an equivalent, no more effortful, readily available and acceptable alternative to the behaviour that is causing others difficulty or upset. To Suzie it was just person-centred common sense.

In a very short space of time Suzie had transformed not only her own thinking but also the attitudes of many of her staff. And it wasn't simply that Suzie no longer saw residents as problems to be managed, let alone seeing them as playing hosts to symptoms of dementia that had to be controlled, she was also committed to improving the lives of the people in her care. What could be done in the hours when they weren't asleep, resting or receiving personal care? Those 11 hours when there are opportunities to give people reasons to be alive, because to live in a care home is to receive more than care. It is also about being provided with a quality of life. The question at the forefront of people's thinking has to be, 'What is the point of getting somebody ready for the day if their day never begins?'

Suzie encouraged lots of one-to-one conversations. Meaningful moments characterised everyone's days. The life stories of residents guided the programme of daily activities and influenced who would participate in what. And if you couldn't come to the activity then whenever possible the activity would go to you. Suzie also introduced activity areas, the most compelling of which was the 'kiddies' nursery'. Located in the corner of a lounge it was resplendent with life-like dolls, a rocking chair, soft toys, a couple of cribs and a changing trolley with a basket of nappies. Were the dolls seen as dolls or babies by those gently rocking or holding them? Who knows? But does it matter? Doll therapy remains controversial – is it demeaning, does it represent treachery

(Kitwood 1997)? – but as an occupational therapist who I hold in high regard once said to me, "I don't do activity, I do happy!" And joyful as well as tranquil moments were observed, and while it was often referred to as the 'mums' zone' one or two men were often seen in the nursery. Of equal note was the observation that at any one time there may have been a dozen women in the lounge, yet only a handful ever walked over to the nursery. The lesson was clear: actions and interventions carried out in the pursuit of making people with dementia feel better must always focus on a person's uniqueness rather than on any stereotypes, assumptions or crass generalisations.

In just a few months so much had changed at Suzie's care home. It became a shining example. Yes, once or twice enthusiasm to try out ideas had got carried away, such as when, in an attempt to dissuade residents from using a door which led to a bedroom hallway, a mouse was painted just above the door handle so it looked for all the world that the mouse was scampering along it. The likeness was certainly a disincentive, but generating alarm and anxiety can never be commended. However, these were isolated exceptions to the good practice that was now in evidence. Yet a conundrum remained. One that was casting a shadow over all Suzie had achieved.

The days in the lives of residents were a joy to behold. The atmosphere was vibrant yet relaxed. Staff had the confidence to use their imagination. The worlds of care and activities were person centred. So much was different, yet evenings were not. Regimented routines and task-led care dominated the actions and outlook of staff. I'd been alerted that all was not well when a routine audit of psychtropic medication revealed an unusually high level use of prn (ie when necessary) antipsychotics, antidepressants and hypnotic medicines commonly prescribed in response to sleep disturbance. It is well known that hypnotics are among the most frequently prescribed, potentially inappropriate, medications in care homes (Fick *et al* 2012) but in this instance I was surprised.

I visited the home one early evening and, bearing in mind on my first visit I'd observed Frances being put into bed at around 6.30pm, I was curious to know whether this was typical, not just for Frances but for other residents too. And it was. Suzie was exasperated. The nurses and carers had not so much slipped back into their old ways, in the evenings they had never actually left them behind. Suzie had spoken to some individually, and had also held a couple of staff meetings. Suzie told them the atmosphere in the evening was not like it was during the day. It was more tense. After their evening meal, what residents wanted appeared to matter less than being taking to the toilet and then being got ready for bed. Some residents became agitated. Unsurprisingly a few were getting up in the early hours having been in bed since early evening. She had heard staff talking about some as being uncooperative, awkward and even aggressive. Language from the old days.

Suzie explained the home didn't have to run like clockwork in the evening. Sleep was important but residents didn't have to be accompanied to their bedrooms so early, and having been put into bed they didn't have to be returned if they got up and were discovered walking the hallways or sitting in the lounge or sitting rooms. And if this meant that the end of the working day was a bit disorganised with residents doing all matter of things that also was fine. "If you work five, ten, even fifteen minutes longer than you should, you can claim all the time back, maybe come in a bit later the next day, or maybe leave early another day." She even divulged her next idea to improve the life of residents – a Night Owl Club. Regardless of whether it was day or night, life had to be good: by introducing a Night Owl Club the night staff would also become involved in the changes that were happening. This was important because Suzie feared that staff who worked nights were on the margins of what was happening, inevitably not feeling included. And if this was so, life at night was always likely to remain institutionalised and impersonal.

The Night Owl Club would start at 10.00pm and would be for residents who had not wanted to go to bed or who had, but then got up. Few were going anywhere the following day and so a late rise or a day in bed would rarely be a problem. And the Night Owl Club would be more than simply accepting that some residents were awake and up at night. It would provide activities and occupation that would not only be enjoyable but would also as hours, maybe just minutes, passed help to tire 'the clubbers' and encourage sleep. It would be held in the lounge and with the main lights subdued and secondary lighting on, a restful and cosy atmosphere could be created. Light snacks would be handed out, a DVD of an old movie could be played or staff could to go to residents' rooms to collect photographs, knick-knacks or mementoes and these could be used as conversational props. Suzie was sure the night staff would like the idea.

The staff had listened and all seemed to agree with what she had to say, but it was always the same, nothing changed. So GPs continued to prescribe medicines such as zolpidem, zaleplon and trazodone for 'disturbed nights', 'insomnia', 'nocturnal wandering' and 'poor sleep'.

Was this happening because the nurses and carers didn't believe Suzie, thinking instead she actually wanted a smooth-running home at the end of the day? Did they ignore her protests because they felt she was wrong and sleep was more important than Suzie thought especially now the days of residents were more active? Might residents prescribed night-time medication actually be struggling with disturbed sleep, as many people with dementia do? Or might the reason lie outside the care home?

Suzie was very single minded and all her energy was focused on improving the lives of her residents. She was on a mission and she could be a force of nature. Considering it was still only a short time since she had been appointed manager, if truth be told her staff still didn't know her well and because of her strong personality none of them had the courage to stand up to her and say how they felt, and how the new ways of working were affecting them.

Nurses and carers don't leave themselves at the front door of the care home when they arrive for work. And nor should they be expected to. Each and every one has a life beyond the workplace. Their home, their family and friends. They have domestic responsibilities, things to do, pleasures to have and plans to make. The evening bus went at five minutes past nine. The day shift ended at nine o'clock. Most got the bus home, which meant they had less than five minutes to get to the bus stop. And if you missed that bus, the timetable switched from a half hour service to an hourly late night service. Fail to get the five past nine bus and you had to wait at the bus stop for nearly an hour, which meant you wouldn't get indoors until after half past ten. As a result, the evenings were dominated by fixed routines because nothing should interfere with the need to be ready to leave the building at nine o'clock on the dot. So Frances, Robert, Emily and nearly all of the others were going to bed early!

We must never forget that there are two groups of people in a care home, those who live in the building, and those who work in it, and both need to be respected and have their voices heard. Unfortunately what many fail to appreciate is that person-centred care applies to everyone, residents, families and even how we work with and approach each other as a team. Suzie had only been addressing one side of the coin. Understandably so, because the needs of her residents were paramount, but if the changes she had introduced were to be sustained they had to be truly accepted and adopted. This meant talking, consulting and listening to her staff, and she hadn't.

Leadership is not about telling others what to do and imposing your ideas. It is about creating a space that others wish to enter as they also come to share the same vision. And this means appreciating the obstacles that might be getting in the way of this happening even when people are sympathetic to what is being proposed. Suzie reflected and *she* changed. Her commitment to transforming what was happening within the walls of the care home continued unabated, but no longer did it feel that the required changes and the need to come up with fresh ideas were her responsibility alone. Although not wrong, Suzie accepted she had been in too much of a hurry to get improvements made. Having realised the error of her ways, the first decision that had to be taken remained hers. The shift timings had to change. Her staff not only agreed, more importantly they felt valued and appreciated for Suzie's decision showed that they and their lives mattered.

The day shift now ends at 8pm. Already the expected has happened. Evenings are no longer frenetic, routines are less apparent, staff are relaxed and the use of prescribed hypnotic medication is dramatically reduced. And the Night Owl Club is up and running. Sometimes the reason why change is resisted can be difficult to understand, because sometimes it is down to the bus timetable.

Bibliography

Baddiel DS (2016) Heard the one about my dad's dementia? *Sunday Times*, 21 February.

Banerjee S (2009) *The use of antipsychotic medication for people with dementia: Time for Action*, HMSO, London.

Batsch NL, Mittelman MS (2012) *Overcoming the stigma of dementia.* World Alzheimer Report 2012, Alzheimer's Disease International, London.

Cheston R, Jones R (2009) A small-scale study comparing the impact of psycho-education and exploratory psychotherapy groups on newcomers to a group for people with dementia. *Ageing and Mental Health* 13 (3) 420-425.

Department of Health (2005). *Mental Capacity Act*. HMSO, London.

Department of Health (2009) *Living Well with Dementia: A national dementia strategy.* HMSO, London.

Fick D, Semla T, Beizer J, Brandt N, Dombrowski R, Dubeau CE *et al* (2012) American Geriatrics Society updated Beers Criteria for potentially inappropriate medication use in older adults. *Journal of the American Geriatrics Society* 60 (4) 616-631.

Hoag S (2014) *A Son's Handbook*. Inspiring Voices, Bloomington.

James I (2011) *Understanding Behaviour in Dementia that Challenges.* Jessica Kingsley, London.

Kitwood T (1990) *Dementia Reconsidered*. Open University, Buckingham.

Moniz-Cook E, Woods RT, Richards K (2001) Functional analysis of challenging behaviour in dementia: the role of superstition. *International Journal of Geriatric Psychiatry* 16 45-56.

Moniz-Cook E, Stokes G, Agar S (2003) Difficult behaviour and dementia in nursing homes: five cases of psychosocial intervention. *Clinical Psychology and Psychotherapy* 10 197-208.

Spector A, Gardner C, Orrell M (2011) The impact of Cognitive Stimulation Therapy groups on people with dementia: views from participants, their carers and group facilitators. *Aging & Mental Health* 2011 1–5.

Stokes G (2000) *Challenging Behaviour in Dementia*. Speechmark, Bicester.

Stokes G (2008) *And Still the Music Plays*. Hawker Publications, London.

Stokes G (2010) The passing of time, in Gilliard J, Marshall M (eds) *Time for Dementia*. Hawker Publications, London.